Forest Ownership for Pleasure and Profit

Forest Ownership for Pleasure and Profit

HARDY L. SHIRLEY AND PAUL F. GRAVES

SYRACUSE UNIVERSITY PRESS

Rural America in Transition

A new type of landowner is rapidly changing the pattern of rural America. He is bringing a different orientation to land ownership than the traditional use for farming or timber harvest. These new owners are not engaged in wresting their basic livelihood from the soil but rather in enjoying the amenities of rural life and the other satisfactions that ownership of a sizeable tract of land can bring.

The opportunity to acquire land has been enhanced markedly by a steady decline in the amount of land in cultivation. The amazing efficiency of modern technology in agriculture, when applied to good land, has so increased farm output that owners of poor lands are unable to compete. Modern technology, however, has also increased the complexity and costs of farming to such an extent that farm management by an absentee owner fully employed elsewhere is no longer feasible.

Far from halting as population has increased, release of land from cultivation has continued since the early forties. Farmers are being encouraged by the U.S. Department of Agriculture to restrict further their cultivated acreage. The federal government itself has acquired land for highways, airports, national parks, and other recreation areas. Suburbia has expanded and with it industrial parks. But much of our land is not suitable or needed for these purposes. Moreover, the very pattern of relatively small rural ownerships makes difficult the acquisition of such land in large tracts suitable for public forests or corporate holdings by wood-using industries. The modest-sized family holding of such forest-oriented rural property seems to have a useful role to play.

Neglected fields east of the Great Plains tend naturally to return to forests over a period of years. Much of the white pine of New England, and the sweet gum and southern pine of the Atlantic Coastal plain, today occupy lands formerly used for agriculture. Two or more tree crops have been harvested from some of these lands since the soil last felt the plow. As agriculture retreats, forests steadily advance. And as farmers move off the land, the new rural owners acquire holdings with one-half or more of the area usually forested.

The new private owners include physicians, lawyers, businessmen, and corporation managers of considerable private income. But also among them are shopkeepers, teachers, steelworkers, farmers who continue to hold but not cultivate the land, and many others who have sought and found varied satisfactions through such ownership.

Understandably, reduction of agricultural acreage and the decrease in the number of farmers has brought economic distress to many rural communities. How may the potential of these lands for forest-related uses be developed to supplement other objectives of owners? What may these new owners do to help sustain the quality of rural life? What does their use of the land contribute to regional and national well-being? These are social and individual questions of some importance. Finding answers to them depends in large part on the motives of the new owners, and these motives appear to be as varied as the owners themselves.

Forest estates are a prominent feature of rural land holdings in Europe. Although many forest estates are but 100 to 150 years old, others originated as feudal or church estates of the medieval period. Land reform movements, which forced feudal owners to give up agricultural lands, allowed them to retain their forests. Forest estates, in fact, were being created by planting up eroded fields at the same time that peasants were clamoring for land to cultivate. Although forests were the source of fuel and other useful products, one of the main incentives for forest ownership was recreation—the joy of the chase. Even today, revenue from shooting rights forms a large part of European forest estate income. That these forest estates have survived and, in fact, have increased in numbers and area during the past century, while considerable pressure of people on the land existed, is significant. It is a clear indication of the many satisfactions their management has yielded the owners, aside from direct money income, and of the economic benefits they have contributed to the nations.

Is it possible that similar desires and economic forces are motivating present-day Americans to create forest holdings of substantial size and permanence as their European cousins have done? If so, how will these holdings fit into the pattern of rural America?

Many of the new owners wish to make their lands—in addition to being a source of income and pleasure to themselves—socially useful and esthetically pleasing to others. The purpose of this book is to help them make their holdings attractive, socially useful, and profitable. It is intended particularly for those owning lands that are already forested or who are considering acquiring relatively wild lands away from major highways. We have explored the motives for ownership, examined the costs and expected returns as well as methods of financing, and have advised the prospective owner about methods and techniques for acquiring and managing a forest estate for pleasure and income.

September 22, 1967   HARDY L. SHIRLEY and PAUL F. GRAVES
Syracuse, New York

CONTENTS

ILLUSTRATIONS

TABLES

Forest Ownership for Pleasure and Profit

Incentives for
Forest Ownership

Man is a complex creature; he seeks to enjoy the advantages to be found in highly organized society—comfortable and convenient living, diversified employment, intensive use of capital in highly mechanized industry, enticing shops offering goods from distant lands, sophisticated entertainment and education, and for some the joy of being part of the throng. But he also seeks quietude—he recognizes his kinship to the land and, so, wishes for part of his active years the freedom of untrammeled space. Americans are fortunate that affluence and modern transportation enable many to indulge both desires. For some, landownership has become a hobby and recreation. Former President Dwight D. Eisenhower has his Gettysburg farm and Thomas Dewey his Pawling dairy, and hundreds of others have landed estates in Dutchess County, New York, or Bucks County, Pennsylvania.

But farming, which is becoming increasingly complex, requires a large initial investment and much day-to-day attention. It does not offer that freedom from responsibility needed to restore buoyance of spirit that the busy salesman, executive, or professional man seeks.

Many may also fail to find satisfaction in the seaside or lakeside vacation lands that have become increasingly popular and increasingly crowded in recent years. The inland lake with its racing outboards, water skiers, loudly tuned radios, and crowded swimming beaches is scarcely a place for relaxation and reflection. The exclusive resort hotel may also lack

1

appeal; its attractions are aimed mainly at overcoming boredom rather than eliciting creative reflection. To people who tire of crowds and commercial entertainment a forest holding offers many unique attractions—privacy, quietude, serenity, and countless diversions to amuse or to stimulate reflection. The forest requires no daily or weekly care. Trees grow year in and year out without cultivation. Although the growth rate of forests is slow, the landowner who has watched a pine plantation develop during its first five to ten years can take deep satisfaction in seeing how the forest has changed the character of his land. There are other amenities of landownership—spending quiet weeks or weekends, fall and winter hunting, fishing if a suitable stream, pond, or lake exists. The forest offers hiking winter and summer, innumerable opportunities for taking pictures, and an opportunity to engage in healthful outdoor exercise. The owner may plant trees, thin the forest, harvest his own fuelwood, or if he is really venturesome, make his own maple syrup.

The forest also offers investment opportunities. Trees do grow, and the growth can be stored on the trees for an indefinite period. When a harvest is made, the income may be treated as a long-term capital gain for federal income tax purposes. Capital can, therefore, be accumulated in the forest during the owner's years of high earnings and drawn upon after his retirement when regular income has declined. Moreover, since the value of timber tends to increase with general commodity prices, forests offer some protection against inflation.

Forest ownership also has some of the qualities of a savings bank account in that capital invested in it accumulates in the form of timber growth that may be withdrawn from time to time. Such withdrawals may be necessary to meet the expenses of a college education or a serious illness or even to pay for a new home.

A productive forest holding also offers the satisfaction of providing a commodity important to our national well-being.

According to a study by the U.S. Forest Service,[1] timber-based activities in the year 1958 accounted for one job in every twenty and one dollar in every twenty dollars of gross national product. The future timber requirements to the year 2000 are estimated to be from 80 per cent to almost 300 per cent above current requirements. Whether such an increased market will, in fact, develop for timber will depend upon the timber supply, itself, and also upon the vigor and imagination with which the forest products industries manufacture and merchandise their products.

Fortunately for those who seek the intrinsic values of forest landownership, many of our great industrial centers are located in or near timber-growing areas. Half of the land of New York and Pennsylvania is covered with forests. In the New England states forests cover as much as 80 per cent of a state's area. Abundant forest land exists in the northern lake states and most of the South. The West Coast has the most magnificent forests of the world.

The well-populated regions offer special opportunities for commercial recreational use of forest land. The operation of game farms, shooting preserves, ski resorts, and vacation enterprises may yield imaginative landowners profit, both directly and indirectly. Many states maintain strong conservation departments and forestry colleges with research programs from which technical advice may be obtained, free or at modest cost, to guide a forest development enterprise. Forest fire control organizations are publicly financed and generally well equipped, and good roads are available in populated regions. Also, where other sources of taxable wealth are available, forest land is less likely to be overtaxed.

Certain other advantages of well-settled regions will be recognized by the man with a speculative turn of mind, for while his timber is growing in volume and value, his land may also be appreciating in value. Urban dwellers, in increasing numbers, are seeking the advantages of a retreat from the crowds and an opportunity to spend part of their time close to the land, so a well-tended forest retreat is likely to have substantial value in its own right.

This is one side of the picture—the alluring side. What of the other side—the risks as well as the opportunities, the headaches as well as satisfactions, the chance for financial loss as well as the prospect for gain?

First, investment in forest lands entails a long-term commitment; liquid capital is not available to be withdrawn on demand. Opportunities for profit are generally long range rather than short range. Timber growth rate is a modest 4 to 10 per cent per year. Taxes and other carrying charges of about one dollar per acre per year may have to be met for several years before the timber reaches sufficient size to justify a merchantable cut. Good timber-growing properties well stocked with merchantable-sized trees are difficult to find and likely to be costly to acquire. Commercial timber accumulates only on trees currently of timber size. Property taxes may bear little relation to the productivity of the land. Forest land, itself, varies widely in productivity for timber crops. Some soils are so thin or infertile that they are wholly unsuitable for growing commercial timber. Other land may support a very favorable growth rate of 400 board feet per acre per year, worth ten dollars or more.

Natural hazards exist—forest fires, tree diseases, insect outbreaks, and even possible damage from windstorms and trespass. Careful, financially responsible loggers can be found, but many fall short of the standards to be desired. Timber markets fluctuate both locally and nationally. Encroachment by undesirable developments is always possible unless holdings are fairly large. Such difficulties need to be recognized. They may deter the timid, but merely challenge the bold.

Motives for Owning Forest Land

We have outlined some of the rewards and challenges of forest ownership in broad terms. Now let us explore some of these in more detail to help clarify the potentialities for owner satisfactions. Of immediate importance to many potential owners are the prospects for financial returns to help carry the costs of the venture. Three owner attitudes may be recognized—those for whom personal satisfactions rather than financial income are the prime objective; those for whom financial income is the chief concern; and those seeking both personal satisfactions and financial returns.

Persons seeking a forest estate as a retreat for work, study, or recreation may have little or no interest in income from the property. Their objective may be, rather, to develop ponds, vistas, wildlife food patches, and personal accommodations; in fact, some people are repelled by the thought of cutting timber, shooting wildlife, or opening their property to fee users. Americans are still fortunate to have sufficient land to accommodate people with such desires. Many of these persons are sensitive, creative individuals for whom the privacy, serenity, and unobtrusiveness of the forest environment is conducive to personal accomplishment. The forest setting may also be appropriate for their leisurely and gracious living and entertainment of intimate friends.

The forest owner whose chief motive is financial return from his property has an entirely different ownership objective. He will want to explore the many possibilities of financial gain from forest landownership, which include:

1) increase in land or timber values,
2) income from sale of forest products,
3) income from land leasing or commercial uses, and
4) certain tax advantages arising from the possibility of deferring income and benefiting from lower tax rates on capital gains.

Since such an owner will be obliged to forego many of the personal pleasures of forest ownership, he must give careful thought to deciding between a forest holding and other investment opportunities having the advantages of lower risk and a higher degree of liquidity.

The majority of professional workers, businessmen, and

corporation executives seem to be seeking primarily personal satisfactions but they, too, have an interest in financial returns. For many, the opportunity for extra income is one of the satisfactions of ownership and certainly one that justifies having an estate larger in area than that needed to provide privacy and seclusion. One may imagine a conflict of interest here, but it need be no more serious than choosing a profession or business because the work has appeal. It does require that a choice must always be made between actions that bring personal satisfactions and those that bring in revenue. Such owners are likely to look askance at leasing rights to others instead of enjoying them personally. On the other hand, they may readily permit timber cutting, harvest of other products, and even limited use by others if that use does not significantly diminish their own satisfactions. Such an owner may be said to be practicing multiple-use management on his land in the same sense that the U.S. Forest Service does so on the national forests

Actually, no clear-cut separation exists between features of a forest estate that bring personal satisfactions and those that can furnish a financial return. If a given feature of the property affords the owner pleasure, like-minded individuals may be willing to pay a fee to enjoy it also. Selling forest products and permitting certain public uses on a fee basis is, after all, but one of the ways of making the land socially useful. The owner, therefore, need not apologize to anyone for realizing an income from his forest property. Let us, therefore, review some of these incentives for ownership, recognizing that many have the potentiality of financial returns as well as personal satisfactions.

Property Improvement

An owner likes to make his personal impress upon his property. He improves the roads, builds trails and overlooks, constructs ponds, stocks fish in streams, and engages in other

An overlook forms a satisfying vantage point for viewing the progress of the owner's plans. Courtesy Niagara Mohawk Power Corp., Eastern Division.

activities that show to him and others that he owns, occupies, and cares for his property. These improvements are satisfying to an owner, for they change a property from what it was to something more nearly what he wants it to be. He probably has learned from foresters or forestry literature that crooked, defective, and diseased trees should be removed, open fields planted, young stands thinned and pruned, and conditions made favorable for wildlife. To accomplish these ends he may make capital investments, on the one hand, and sell timber, on the other.

If he cuts his timber conservatively, the residual trees are improved in quality and over the years increase in volume and value. He may also look forward to an increase in timber prices equivalent to the rise in the general price level and possibly somewhat more as timber demands grow with increasing population. His land may also increase in value, both as a result of increased price level and of the demonstration by himself and others of the satisfactions offered by forest ownership. This dual financial return from timber growth and general price increase adds to the attractiveness of owning a forest property.

Marketing Products

Forest products include wood, water, wildlife, Christmas trees, maple products, recreational value, and such minor items as greenery, pharmaceutical plants, fruits, and nuts. Forest land may also have commercial deposits of sand, gravel, rock, and various minerals that could become sources of revenue. Most forests are renewable through growth and hence are capable of affording income for the indefinite future. Harvesting mature trees to open the forest for regrowth brings the multiple satisfactions of monetary returns and making the forest more vigorous and hospitable to wild creatures. Selling Christmas trees, greenery, and other forest products also gives the owner the satisfaction of making his property yield further revenue, as well as adding to the local economy.

Encouraging Wildlife

The owner and his family may have a real interest in wildlife and seek to favor it by erecting shelters, birdhouses, and feeding stations and planting food and cover plants. He may even go beyond this to stock game and fish and develop the type of tree and vegetative cover that will favor high wildlife density. To carry this line of thought to its logical extreme, he might even operate a game farm, either for personal pleasure or for profit. Without going quite this far, the owner might lease hunting rights or allow fee hunting during periods when he is absent from the property.

Restricted Use by Others

Most of us enjoy entertaining and take pride in being able to offer pleasant facilities to our friends. Certainly the forest estate offers unique entertainment possibilities in winter, summer, spring, and fall. The charm of the forest and rural environment at all seasons of the year is feelingly portrayed in Aldo Leopold's *Sand County Almanac* as well as in Henry Thoreau's *Walden Pond*. Friends may, in fact, enjoy the experience so much that they will want to buy the adjoining property or lease a site on their host's land. This is one of the risks involved in entertaining, for the abutting property may be one the owner himself has had his eye upon; he may console himself, however, because of the opportunity of sharing certain expenses with his erstwhile guest.

The new owner may even become the second member of an exclusive club, and what began as cost sharing may be turned into substantial income. For example, an owner may find a happy compromise by leasing certain rights to a private club of which he is a member. Such clubs, if limited in membership and interested mainly in riding, hiking, skiing, picnicking, hunting, fishing, and bathing, may cause no significant interference with timber growth, cutting operations, or sale of other forest products. Some such clubs have substantial membership dues—$500 to $1,000 per year for family use. Such a revenue makes possible generous services to members and a fair rental fee to the landowner.

An alternate opportunity for reducing costs is to work out a plan for joint sharing of benefits and expenses through a multifamily association or club. Several such associations have already been formed. They provide possibilities for much greater social life and greater amenities than can be provided on an individual basis. Decision making on investments, sales, and expenses then becomes an association, rather than a family, prerogative. Associations of this type have qualified for public loans for water systems and sewage treatment under the Food and Agriculture acts of 1962 and 1965.

Fee Use

A step beyond leasing to friends or a club is opening the land to restricted use by the public for an appropriate fee. By providing a suitable parking spot, the proprietor may charge fees for entering upon the land for trail riding, hiking, picnicking, birdwatching, visiting a nature trail, or other activities. The fee system requires some supervision and maintenance. The system may be operated on an honor basis by simply erecting a suitable box with an appropriate sign showing the schedule for fees. Frequent visits by the owner or his agent may be required to assure compliance with rules.

Overnight Camping

Privately operated campgrounds open to the public for a fee have developed rapidly in the past five years and seem destined to become a growing use for private forests. Practical operation of such a campground, however, becomes a full-time job for the owner and one or more helpers during the camping season. Individuals who have their summers free can gain income and satisfactions from such an operation. A minimum economic size is some two hundred campsites. Requisites include a swimming area, pool for small children, safe drinking water, sanitary facilities, and a grocery supply store. This becomes a business in itself during the camping season.

Leasing Forest Land

A forest property may be leased for a variety of uses—hunting, camp and summer home sites, or day use by organizations or clubs for riding, hiking, picnicking, skiing, and related outdoor sports. Revenue may also be had from leasing rights-of-way for power and gas lines, roads, and for various forms of public use such as scenic easements. Timber rights, too, may be leased. It is possible, of course, to lease the entire property for a private shooting ground, a resort, or other purpose. The favorability of such possibilities depend, first, upon the owner finding a lessee, and secondly upon the value of the property to the prospective user. Although certain leasing uses are compatible one with another, others require exclusive use.

Increase in Land and Timber Values

Forest land, in common with other real estate, tends to increase in value with time. While this is a general trend, it is by no means universal. In areas being released from cultivation, values may continue to decline for one or more decades. Timber values also tend to rise over the years. But unless local timber is abundant enough to support a thriving industry, the market may decline rather than improve with time. An investor depending upon increased land and timber values is speculating upon a trend of economic events none can foresee. If he is shrewd in his purchases, he may realize substantial financial gain. A high degree of risk is involved, however.

Deferred and Capital Gain Taxation

The owner of forest property may deduct land taxes from current personal income. If his property is operated entirely as a business enterprise, other business expenses on the property may also be deductible. Business expenditures judiciously made will lead to future income, much of which may be delayed to retirement years. Income from timber sales is eligible for capital gains treatment, thereby offering the double incentive of deferment and lower taxation to the man in high income brackets.

Although a forest property may offer numerous potential sources of revenue, some are far more readily realizable than others. Income from timber sales is by far the most reliable. That from leasing hunting and fishing rights is dubious, except on larger properties, and leasing to an exclusive club for a flat fee depends a good deal upon providing of artificial as well as natural attractions. Income from sale of water is a remote possibility. Unless the owner can realize his objectives through personal satisfactions augmented by revenue from sale of timber, he may need to explore prospects other than those of forest property ownership.

The Motive to Create

Perhaps the most constructive and also most widespread motive among the new forest owners is to do something creative with their property. A man who has transformed a misused or unproductive area of forest and rural land into a healthy and contributing setting with a growing forest and other assets has created something, just as a farmer did a century ago when he carved a productive farm out of the wilderness. While a man may gain pleasure by pitting his skill against opponents in skiing, golf, bridge, or other games, many individuals gain abiding satisfactions through activities that benefit society as well as themselves. To such individuals, commonplace amusements may seem frivolous when compared with seeing a forest environment transformed under their ministrations.

Personal Motives and Objectives

The individual must fit the above motives for forest ownership to his personal situation. For the owner and the land he acquires, there is a joining of futures for a long time to come, preferably for life. Quick returns are unlikely. He, therefore, must see his forest holding as a part of his life from the time of acquisition on out. He should recognize that while the forest may be an ideal family vacation spot for children between the ages of five and fifteen, it has its drawbacks for a mother with babies to care for and, perhaps, for teenagers who seek the companionship of youths their own ages. Those whose employment involves frequent transfers may find a forest property to be a burden they can ill afford. For these, membership in an association or club managing forest land may be more appropriate.

Family Situation

A forest property should fit into the family scheme of living as well as into family financial planning; otherwise the costs and responsibilities of acquisition and ownership exceed the pleasures and financial returns. For some people, desirable tracts may be available within commuting distance of their place of work, making possible resident ownership and occupancy. Such an individual has the possibility of maximum returns in personal satisfaction and minimum custodial expense. For others the property may be close enough for weekend use, and for still others it may serve as a summer home for the family.

The prospective owner, therefore, should review his objectives with the needs of his family in mind. Questions such as the following require consideration:

Would my wife and children share my interest and enthusiasm for having a forest estate of our own?

Do they have a love of the out-of-doors and a desire to work constructively with trees, landscape, and land resources?

Do I want my children to develop a feeling for the land and to have the satisfactions of seeing results of physical accomplishment through our combined efforts?

What role can the forest property play in the education and maturing of my children and their preparation for meeting the obligations of life?

Will I have the time to spend on the property to manage it profitably and to realize personal and family satisfactions commensurate with the cost, effort, and risk involved?

Would there be a sense of gratification and pride in personal land ownership?

Would the property become a serious financial burden or a source of anxiety to my wife and children should I die?

Some parents feel that summer vacation periods for children should not be devoted solely to play. Such indulgence, they feel, tends to give children an exaggerated opinion of their own importance and of the significance of their own wishes. Or, to the more thoughtful child, it may produce boredom and a certain sense of frustration in that nothing he does seems very useful either to himself or to his parents. The opportunity to work constructively with a piece of land—planting trees, surveying boundaries, estimating timber volumes and values, building a dam for a family pool, shaping Christmas trees for the market, harvesting fuelwood, and even marking trees to be harvested and making a timber sale—these constructive tasks add zest to a growing boy's day and may cause him to dream of his playing a significant role in broader activities in the future. Moreover, if he can participate in the growing and sale of Christmas trees or other products for which he receives a share of the returns, he will understand more fully the reasons for investment, saving, and work in today's world.

Financial Situation

The owner should realize that his investment in a forest property not only requires considerable capital outlay at the beginning but also entails annual operating expenses for taxes, custodianship, consulting services, legal fees, and management development that must be met for many years. Initially, income for current expenses may be limited. Prospective owners should consider carefully how much they are prepared to commit to capital investment and how much to operating costs, weighing these against present financial resources and the future outlook. And such an owner must expect the property to require his personal attention in many management decisions.

Assuming a property of 500 acres at a cost of about twenty dollars per acre, the total outlay may run as high as $15,000 when costs of title examination and clearance, surveying, timber estimating, boundary marking, and examining and rejecting unsuitable parcels are included. To this must be added the cost of camp, dwelling, or other structures suited to family needs. When tree planting is desired or needed on portions of the land, an additional twenty to twenty-five dollars per acre will have to be spent. The owner may consider growing Christmas trees to obtain early financial returns, but this requires additional investment for planting, weeding, and shearing the trees. Even for Christmas trees, there is a seven-to ten-year delay before harvest.

Custodianship

Every form of property requires care and protection by the owner. A summer home may be broken into by vandals or thieves. Even standing timber may be cut and hauled away if the timber thief knows it is held by an absentee owner having no local person in charge. Special protection can be provided by employing a local caretaker or part-time custodian to visit the property from time to time and report promptly any damage that may be done. Just the fact of having a local man in charge who knows the people of the neighborhood discourages acts of vandalism or thieving. The peace of mind he affords the owner may well justify his retainership. The need for protection should be given thought in selecting the property location, in weighing costs of ownership, and in deciding whether to own the land or simply to lease it for recreational use.

Unless an aspirant owner can afford to meet such financial obligations without depriving himself and his children of other advantages he would wish them to have, he may be obliged to forego owning a forest property.

He will need also to bear in mind that if personal use looms large in activities on his forest estate, he should give thought to how this may appear to the Internal Revenue Service if deductions for business costs are contemplated. The tax examiner is schooled at uncovering vacation or other recreational expenses presented as legitimate costs of operating a business. The owner must be prepared to separate personal expenses for family recreation from defensible business costs and investment. Not having a summer camp on the land is a good argument with the tax examiner but may limit one's enjoyment of the property. It is wise to seek the advice of a qualified accountant in keeping cost records and preparing tax returns if the property is to serve the dual purpose of family recreation and business investment.

One should recognize also that a limit exists to the extent that a forest property may be used for diverting current income, from which the income tax collector otherwise takes a large bite, into long-term investment on which only capital gains tax must be paid. This feature of the law permitting lower rates for revenues classifiable as capital gains was considered for rescinding while the 1964 tax law was in bill form.

Consistency of Objectives

A property that may have superb scenery, such as a mountain setting overlooking other mountains and lakes, may often be found to have thin soil, be windswept, and for other reasons be low in timber productivity. Lowlands and swamps may abound in insect pests, even though they also feature waterfowl or rare wildflowers. One can rarely have on a single property, unless it is a large one, a wide enough variety of conditions to fill every real or imagined desire. Hence, careful analysis of these is necessary to reach sound decisions.

The reader will have learned from the foregoing that a forest property cannot be loaded with excessive overhead or luxury costs and still be expected to pay out financially. It may provide a hunting retreat for the owner and friends, but it must do so on a modest cost basis if one expects a return on the property investment. If recreational use overshadows by far the satisfaction to be derived from building up the productivity of the forest property as such, it might be well to consider to what extent forest landownership is a requisite for the type of recreational use desired.

Providing for Inheritance

The owner should also consider what is to be done with the

property upon his death. Ideally, the forest holding would be passed on to heirs interested in managing it as a forest estate. Here again, tax considerations enter into the decision. The investor, himself, may hold the property during many years while costs exceed income by a considerable margin, charging the costs off against his personal income. But should he die, the property is subject to appraisal as a part of his estate on which inheritance taxes must be paid. Unless his estate is ample to cover such taxes, the property may have to be divided or sold, even though the owner may have thought of it as a part of his personal insurance for the family.

By incorporating the forest estate as a family-held corporation and distributing stock ownership to his wife and children, the owner may minimize inheritance taxes, but he may also lose the opportunity of writing off current costs against personal income. The advice of an estate and tax lawyer should be sought by a prospective owner or forest holder before he commits himself beyond what is prudent for a man of his particular age, health, and financial resources.

Professional Help Needed

The overview given above of a forest property purchasing and management is sufficient to alert the prospective purchaser that he will need professional help if he is to avoid costly mistakes. Further reference is made to such need throughout this book. Suggestions for selecting and benefiting from professional help is given in the Appendix, pages 192-95.

SUMMARY

Forest ownership has many attractions to offer. Among these are seclusion, privacy, and other amenities of a forest environment; the enjoyment of uncrowded space and healthful exercise; the opportunity to invest time and money in property improvement and see it gradually transformed to fit the owner's desires. It offers opportunities for family enterprise which can be instructive, give children a sense of participation in an important activity, afford earning possibilities for school expenses and personal needs, and develop a sense of the importance of work and saving.

It offers income possibilities from sale of forest products and leasing of hunting and other rights. It offers some hedge against inflation and some possibilities for income deductions for costs incurred during his earning years to be recouped later as long-term capital gains.

Forest landownership, however, requires long-term investment; such an investment should be made only after careful consideration of the obligations being assumed and the returns likely to accrue to self and family. Professional consultants will be needed to guide the enterprise.

LITERATURE CITED

1. Dwight Hair, *The Economic Importance of Timber in the United States,* U.S. Department of Agriculture, Forest Service, *Miscellaneous Publication 941,* illustrated (Washington, D.C., 1963), 91.

II

Financing the Forest Estate

In 1820, Zachariah Allen purchased abandoned farmland in Rhode Island which he planted to oak, chestnut, and locust. During the next fifty-seven years he sold $4,948 worth of timber that yielded him a return of 12.93 per cent per annum on his investment. Others have followed his lead with gratifying financial returns. A public forest officer began investing in timberlands following his retirement at age seventy. During the ensuing fifteen years he built up a property in excess of five thousand acres that increased the value of his capital fivefold. A lumberman in New York State began planting abandoned fields to pine trees around the turn of the century. Earnings from these plantations paid his heir 3 per cent on the investment during the depression years of the thirties. The property has increased vastly in value since then. A forester acquired some sixty thousand acres of tax delinquent lands in the Lake States during the depressed 1930's. Two decades later their sale to a timber company made him independently wealthy.

Today the property owner needs to be more clearly cognizant of his financial obligations and potentials than ever before. Costs and carrying charges are higher, predictability of events is lower, and adjustments of the owner to financial needs both for the property and for his family are more frequent. Financial considerations are usually the most critical element in determining suitability of the entire landownership undertaking. The nature of costs and returns for the desired level of activity on the forest property should be matched against the owner's expectations, his alternative interests, and the availability of his financing.

Adjusting Operations to Financial Capacity

While forest estate ownership is by no means as widespread in the United States as in European countries, it has now come within financial reach of a large portion of our population and the number of people able to afford the investment is rapidly expanding. Large family holdings of forest areas, common for generations in parts of the East, have generally been profitable investments. Management costs and taxes have been low, forest operations extensive, and division of properties into small holdings usually avoided.

Elsewhere individuals have built up successful forest holdings by buying prudently and avoiding expensive development costs. Financing has been from personal savings, from timber sales, and by keeping borrowing well within capacity to repay. Examples can be cited in the Northeast, the Lake States, the South, and the West Coast where careful investments in forest properties have established modest family fortunes. For such forest landowners the lean years during acquisition and building up the property have been well compensated through generous returns during the second and third decades. The keys to success have been acquiring substantial areas of low-cost forest land with good tree-growing capability, keeping current costs for financing and operations as low as possible consistent with proper attention to growth potentials, harvesting but part of the annual timber growth, and reinvesting some earnings into expanded land holdings and prudent forest improvement. A few have been able to benefit from public financial aids, but most have achieved their success through their own financial resources and management efforts. It is interesting also that most such estates were built up while their owners were performing full-time services in business, the professions, or in government employment.

Except for lands that have speculative possibilities, the owners should not expect forest properties to triple or quadruple in value over a ten- to fifteen-year period. Patience, faith, careful planning, and alertness to opportunities are essential for success in forest land operations, the same as they are in most business enterprise. Above all, the forest owner must guard against overcommitment on capital costs. Each prospective owner should consider his present and possible future tax position, his willingness to make a long-term commitment, and the inflationary trends of our economy, as well as the immediate cost outlays. It may well be that the forest investment will prove to be fully as attractive as any other opportunity available to him and more enjoyable to him and his family.

Nature of Costs

To build a forest land estate that is to be operated to any degree for financial gain requires the keeping of appropriate records. These are necessary to keep track of the business aspects of the property and to support necessary reports. If family recreation is involved, these records should clearly differentiate between costs of the two activities. Deciding which costs may appropriately be considered as legitimate business expenses and which ones are personal is not always easy. Hence, records not only of the purposes for which costs were incurred, but of what the owner did on each visit to his property may be needed to support his tax claim for business expenses.

For his own sake, the estate owner must differentiate also between capital costs and operating costs. Capital costs are those that increase the long-range value of the property, including its capacity to produce income. Operating costs are those incurred to maintain the property and in the production of income. Capital costs on forest property include expenditures for the following:

1) Land and buildings.

2) Acquisition costs including survey, title examination, title opinion, commissions, boundary survey, and costs of examining the timber, including a timber estimate if the estimate is made in advance of purchase. Generally, it would include all legal and consulting costs incurred in the acquisition of the property and the recording of the deed.

3) Improvements. Existing buildings, nonpublic roads, fences, telephone and power lines, ponds, landscaping, etc., that were acquired with the land are obviously a part of the capital cost. Those that are constructed after acquisition are also considered capital costs and should be carried on the books as such. This would include a family camp or summer home, swimming pool, ponds, and structures erected for rental purpose, such as campground improvements, cabins for rent and the appurtenances thereto, water development, sewer system, private access roads, and similar costs.

4) Forest plantations. If the owner plants vacant lands and fields to trees, the cost of this plantation is considered a capital investment.

5) Timber. All timber growing on the land at the time of acquisition is considered a part of the real estate and, therefore, a part of the capital investment.

6) Equipment. Equipment would include forestry and office instruments such as surveying instruments and drafting sets, automotive equipment, power saws, and generally durable items costing in excess of ten dollars that would have a useful life of five or more years. Handbooks and forestry texts acquired by the owner would fall into this category.

7) Capital appreciation and returns. The capital value of the property appreciates through timber growth. It may also appreciate because of increases in land and timber values. For simplified accounting, however, it is best to establish base prices for land and for timber at the beginning and adhere to these in accordance with generally accepted account-

ing practices, throughout the ownership period. Such base prices would be retained even though the value of the timber might be considerably increased by the owner's action in removing low-quality trees and concentrating the growth on those of higher value.

Capital diminishes owing to resource depletion, equipment depreciation, and sale of basic assets. When timber is sold, the total value of the property is diminished, and a portion of the capital value may be charged off due to depletion. Each item of equipment will have a basic useful life. For an item having a useful life of five years, one-fifth the cost may be charged off the capital value each year. When an item is sold that has been fully depreciated, the net income from the sale is treated as income. If buildings, land, gravel, or minerals are sold from the property, a reduction in capital value occurs and should be shown on the account books for the property.

Operating Costs

Operating costs are those incurred to maintain the property and to conduct operations that produce income from it. They include:

> Taxes
> Insurance
> Maintenance of roads and structures
> Custodianship and protection
> Supplies
> Keeping the timber estimates up to date
> Costs of making timber sales
> Supervisory and management costs.

Taxes are an annual expense about which only one certainty exists: they are more likely to increase than decrease. Oftentimes when lands now in forest have formerly been cultivated, the tax assessor continues them on the tax rolls at the higher farm rate. It is well to determine the taxes on a property before acquiring it, and to decide whether or not the timber growth is likely to be sufficient to cover the taxes and other carrying charges. School taxes, real estate taxes, and special assessments are all part of the annual operating costs, whether paid at one time or in separate billings during the year.

Normally, the "supplies" category includes postage, stationery, field notebooks, drafting supplies, maps, aerial photos, and other office supplies. It also includes such hand tools as pruning saws, axes, shovels, surveying pins, and other items consumed during operations. The distinction between equipment and supplies is not always easy to determine.

Costs of making a timber sale include marking the trees and estimating the timber volume to be cut, advertising and negotiating a sale, drawing a contract, supervising logging operations and collecting from the operator, and paying any commissions that may be involved.

Management costs are those incurred by the owner for general supervision of all forest operations, including both planning and execution. They include also costs of professional services for accounting, legal advice, and consulting forester fees.

Operating Income

Operating income includes net return from such items as the following:

    Sale of timber (note below)

    Sale of minor products such as ferns, greenery, fruits, nuts, and water

    Sale of Christmas trees

    Rentals from pasture, campsite, and cabins

    Leasing of hunting rights

    Income from related enterprises such as campground or game farm operation.

As noted above, income from timber sales may be considered partly depletion of capital, but only in the proportion that the volume cut bears to the total volume. For example, if the owner acquired 1,000,000 board feet of timber which cost him, exclusive of land costs, $10,000, and if he sold 100,000 board feet for $2,000, he could charge to depletion but one-tenth his total timber cost, or $1,000. The remaining $1,000 must be treated as income. Even so, after making ten such sales he would have exhausted his depletion base, and thereafter all revenue from timber sold would have to be treated as income. The capital gains tax would still apply to this income, however, assuming that this feature remains on the statutes.

The price an owner can afford to pay for a forest property depends on the net income it can be expected to yield on invested value under the type of management he is prepared to give it. It also depends upon what the amenities the forest affords are worth to himself and to his family in personal satisfactions. It is, therefore, appropriate to consider the potential sources of income in more detail and to estimate the likelihood of this income being realized by the average owner.

Forestry, like most businesses, requires careful attention to details, wise choice of alternatives in expenditures, development of good markets, and proper control over operating costs. Because the number of business decisions made during the year is likely to be small relative to other businesses, a forest business can be handled on a spare-time basis. This is one of its attractions to an investor.

Income from Water, Wildlife, and Forage

Forests provide wood, water, wildlife, forage, and recreational opportunities. They conserve and build up soil. They tend to reduce peak runoff of flood waters and to maintain the soil in an open, porous condition that favors replenishment of ground water supplies. They give a pleasing appearance to the landscape. The mixed forests of hardwoods and conifers present a dazzling sight in their autumn coloration and attract thousands of visitors from urban areas. To what extent are these several products and services of forests merchantable commodities that may benefit the individual landowner?

Standing timber, at least that of merchantable size, is recognized by everyone as the property of the landowner, and he is protected by law in this right. Minor products of the land such as native ferns, mushrooms, wild nuts, and fruits also are the property of the landowner, but usually the owner makes no charge to those who gather them. Game belongs to the state. A man may lease hunting privileges and fishing rights to another man or to a game club, but the wild game animals and birds may not, themselves, be sold by the owner. Since industrial owners who lease the hunting rights on their forest land generally do so for no more than the property taxes on the land, the small property owner is unlikely to realize a higher fee.

Few forest owners are in a position to gain revenue from any of the public services their forest management provides in terms of soil protection, flood control, recharging of ground water supplies, and flow of water from the land. Benefits from these services accrue mostly to downstream residents who have enjoyed them over many years and cannot be assessed for their continuance.

Only in a few cases in which the forest estate comprises a complete watershed from which a municipality, an industrial plant, or some other specific user draws his supplies may the landowner expect to benefit financially from the water potential of his land. In rare cases, however, there may be an undeveloped spring water source which may be sold to a village or a firm as a water supply.

Forests in the northeastern United States furnish no commercial forage for domestic livestock. Limited forage is produced in southern pine forests and in the open forests of western states. The grazing fees on such lands, generally modest, are a questionable source of income from which to support the forest as it grows to maturity. Also, the income to be derived must be balanced against the reduction in timber growth that results from the trampling of animals and their browsing on valuable young tree seedlings. This potential damage by animals implies the need for some control, probably in the form of fencing. For properties made up mainly of small holdings, the costs of such fencing and other control measures are likely to leave little to cover other costs of ownership. If the owner happens to acquire open meadow land with his forest holdings, he may sell the hay crop or permit grazing. Since some open land provides a break in cover type and creates edge conditions useful for wildlife, and as it provides an unobstructed view, it adds much charm to the landscape. In the eastern United States such lands will be invaded gradually by tree cover unless pastured or mowed periodically. The landowner might well enjoy keeping some of the land open for these purposes. His annual income from pasture rental and hay crops may match that from his forest land, at least during the early years while the forests are being restored to higher productivity.

Recreation

Attempts to realize financial gain for recreation use of the forest, other than by leasing of hunting and fishing rights, will also probably be abortive unless the owner enters into the recreation business, as such, has one thousand acres or more, or is able to link his land with adjoining owners' and lease it for certain recreation uses. In any case, recreational use by others may interfere to some extent with his own objectives in holding the land and will likely limit the scope for managing the property for timber production.

Maple Sugar Operations

The American public has rather romantic notions about the manufacture of maple syrup and sugar. The process is carried out in the early spring while snow is still lying in the woods,

Collecting maple sap on snowshoes is an invigorating task. Note the plastic pipe line which conveys the sap to the sugar house.

in the northern regions where sugar maple trees are abundant. It involves vigorous outdoor exercise in tapping the trees, hanging the pails, collecting sap, stoking the fire under the evaporator, and drawing off and straining the finished product. Maple sugar operations are covered in several bulletins of state extension services and other publications.[1,2]

Maple products manufacture does represent a good potential source of income if it can be integrated into some other year-round operation; otherwise, the nonresident owner will find that his costs are high and his net income negative. There is one ceiling which prevails over the industry, the price that the consumer is willing to pay for syrup. Prices over the last two decades have ranged from about four to seven dollars a gallon, with higher price prevailing for only a few years. Unless the forest owner can produce syrup profitably for retail sale at a price of five dollars per gallon, he had better not attempt this business. The major item of cost is for labor.

Christmas Trees

Commercial Christmas tree growing, when initiated in the eastern states before World War II, was carried on by relatively few growers on a large-scale operation. Since 1945, a great number of farmers and others have set out Christmas tree plantations. Depending upon the species used and the sizes to which the trees are grown, harvesting may begin as early as six to eight years for Scotch pine and table-sized balsam fir, and at eight to thirteen years for other trees. A grower can expect to harvest about one hundred trees per acre per year, operating on a twelve- to fifteen-year rotation plan. Christmas trees have brought an average of about one dollar per tree standing in the plantation during the period 1950-62, and prices for choice specimens have gone as high as $4.50 per tree. The market price, however, has dropped considerably since peak years, and the likelihood of a further drop seems evident as more people get into the business and more substitutes appear.

It does not take much calculation, at one hundred trees per acre per year, to realize that some 40,000-50,000 acres could supply all the trees consumed in a state as populous as New York. The entire nation could easily be supplied by the output of 600,000 acres. There are estimated to be some fifty million acres of submarginal farm land available for Christmas tree planting, and it is obvious that not all of it can be devoted to this purpose. Furthermore, most Christmas trees are harvested from natural forest stands in Canada, the Lake States, and the West.

Christmas tree growing has certain other drawbacks aside from the investment in the tree seedlings and the work involved in setting them out on old fields. They require a certain amount of attention; they must be protected from fire and insects and from hardwood competition should the field already be partially grown up; they must be sheared annually to develop thick-foliaged trees of symmetrical shape; they must be marketed at the right age, or else they get too large or too poor in appearance to command the top price; and the plantation must be protected against trespass during the weeks immediately preceding Christmas.

While a Christmas tree operation could be of almost any size, one of fifty to one hundred acres is likely to be much more profitable financially than one of ten acres or less. Evergreens suitable for Christmas trees include balsam and other true firs, Douglas fir, white spruce, and Scotch pine.

Further information on Christmas tree growing is available.[3,6] Christmas tree growers have an association, membership in which would be helpful to people who enter the business. State foresters and extension services can furnish names and addresses of local officers.

Other Products

A variety of minor products are harvested from forests, including nuts, fruits, pharmaceutical plants, ferns, club mosses, Christmas greens, oil of wintergreen and other flavoring extracts, Canada balsam, pine gum for turpentine and rosin, fence posts, poles and piling, crossties, bolts for excelsior, and bolts for veneer products such as tongue depressors and ice cream spoons. The number of products is high, and when there is a market, prices are generally attractive. Market potential for all these is worth looking into by an owner whose property produces such materials. To illustrate how specialty markets for trees may affect their value and, hence, the gross income available to the landowner, the following comparisons are worthy of note. A balsam fir at ten years of age may make a Christmas tree worth one dollar. If left to grow to pulpwood size at forty years, it would bring twenty cents. The gross potential income per acre per year for Christmas trees would be one hundred dollars, for pulpwood two dollars. A loblolly pine tree at sixty years that would produce a fifty-foot piling would be worth fifty dollars peeled and loaded on a truck, for sawtimber it would be worth $4.80. An understanding of the prices of various products, therefore, can give an important advantage to the alert forest owner.

The one drawback to such specialty markets is their sparsity and limited nature. An owner would be fortunate, indeed, to have a profitable outlet for more than one such type of product.

Other Values

In addition to the values of good forest management, mentioned above, are social values. These include those of making the land productive through improvement activities, thereby increasing the yield of timber which, when harvested, provides jobs for wage earners and raw material for industry. These values accrue to society, but society currently furnishes the owner no direct financial return for such responsible custodianship; in fact, it may lead to an increase in his property assessment, and certainly not to its reduction.

One additional public value is provided that may or may not

bring monetary returns to the owner. This is the esthetic value. Some states pay a fee for scenic easements, provided the owner agrees to keep the land free of buildings and other improvements. Such easements are likely to increase in popularity as the public comes to appreciate the values of a natural landscape.

The absentee woodland owner is, therefore, left with two major choices:

1) Go into the commercial recreation business, himself, or lease his land to others for this purpose. He thereby surrenders most of his personal use of the property, at least for the recreational season.

2) Content himself with the income he can expect from timber production.

He will, therefore, desire to look into the wood market with some care. Immediately the importance of scale of operation must be considered, for wood standing in the forest is not a high-priced commodity.

Size of Estate

A study was made by Resources for the Future, a private nonprofit research corporation, of the economic handicaps faced by the small forest landowner. Although this study was made primarily as a basis for formulating policies for public action to increase the timber yields from land in small ownerships, it does indicate some of the handicaps that the owners of small properties face when their major ownership objective is commercial timber production. Charles H. Stoddard, the author of this bulletin,[4] characterized the economic prospects for forestry based on size alone as follows. For properties under 100 acres, economic prospects are deemed to be poor to nonexistent unless the plot is combined with other ownerships for management purposes or with other enterprises. For 100-500 acres, economic prospects are considered to be fair. Such properties, if well stocked and under some form of group or supervised management, can be expected to meet operating expenses. If poorly stocked, and especially if near the lower limit in size, the prospects are not good. They offer little in the way of investment return.

Properties 500 to 5,000 acres in size offer fair to good economic prospects as individual units. If the land has been carefully selected, and if skilled management is used, the owner can expect fair to good returns.

Owners holding 5,000 to 50,000 acres have good prospects for managing them successfully. Properties larger than 15,000 acres in size can support the services of an organization to provide protection and management, including the harvesting and marketing of products.

While Stoddard's bulletin was prepared on the basis of forest conditions on a nationwide basis, his conclusions concerning the importance of size should be carefully studied by anyone contemplating going into the timber growing business. In growing wood for financial income, certain factors, therefore, are of paramount importance—size of property, timber species and quality, soil and other factors determining growth rate, general timber stand condition, and markets for the various types of products that the forest can produce. A man planning to purchase a forest for income should expect to acquire a minimum of five hundred acres, and preferably more.

Market Potential for Timber

Wood, contrary to public opinion, is not a scarce commodity in the United States; its rate of replacement through growth exceeds current consumption. It is the quality of standing timber that has declined as the old-growth stands have been harvested and small-sized second growth has taken their place. In overview for our nation in its entirety, a decline in timber volume occurred from the year 1492, when the original total volume is estimated to have been 5,200 billion board feet, to 1945, when a low of 1,601 billion board feet was reached. Thereafter, some increase has accrued to 1,968 billion board feet in 1953 and some 2,537 billion board feet in 1963. The rate of growth was still accelerating in 1966.[5]

Forest land also has been increasing in area since about 1910 because of the abandonment of poor farmland to forest. From 1933 to 1953, total forest land in the United States increased by 33,000,000 acres, and the process still continues.

Lumber production, the chief commercial use of forests in the United States, reached a peak in the year 1908 of some 45 billion board feet. Since then, except for depression years, it has fluctuated between 30 and 40 billion board feet. Use of wood for fuel has virtually disappeared except in a few rural areas and as a luxury item for modern homes with fireplaces. Wood used for railway ties, cooperage, boxes and crates, and posts and poles has also declined since the turn of the century. Changes in labor costs and technology relative to other products have been one cause. These uses also have declined to some extent because of the high cost of lumber and other wood products and the difficulties of effecting substantial economies in harvesting and manufacturing owing to declining quality of standing timber. Lumber, since 1860, has increased in price more rapidly than other building materials and more rapidly than commodities in general. Whatever the reasons, and they are many, the lumber market has not kept abreast of the general economy for decades and seems unlikely to stage a brisk upsurge on a nationwide basis soon. High-quality lumber commands strong and increasing market prices, however.

The market for pulp and paper and veneer and plywood has followed an opposite trend. Total use and per capita use has grown rapidly and uninterruptedly since these industries were founded in the United States. The use of these products seems likely to continue to expand in the future. Unfortunately, veneer and plywood require the highest quality logs, and these are seldom obtainable from second-growth forests. Pulpwood, on the other hand, is abundant in most areas, causing prices for stumpage, trees standing in the forest, to remain low.

The sawmills, for all their shortcomings, remain, therefore, the chief market for timber products throughout the United States. The question arises concerning the potential of the sawtimber market. This is a subject for conjecture: Many promising features exist—a rapidly-growing population, a return of wood to favor in many markets temporarily lost to metals and plastics, an expanding scientific wood technology that makes possible treating wood to render it fire resistant and resistant to insect attack and decay and treating to render it plastic and, hence, bendable and capable of being densified. Also, new forms and shapes have been fabricated to add stiffness and strength for beams and laminated arches. Certainly the market outlook for lumber of good quality is encouraging. New methods of sawing logs and handling lumber are also adding to the efficiency of the lumber industry. A national program to standardize sizes and grades will be a help to the construction industry and architects. Use of modern electronic methods to stress grade lumber is an innovation making possible greater precision in designing structures to be built of wood, and the grading system, by supplying new engineering data, may make it possible to recapture structural uses given up by architects because of the wide variability in strength of wood of lower grades.

A nationwide promotion campaign sponsored by the National Forest Products Association is emphasizing the intrinsic merits of wood for many uses. For example, the slowness of wooden beams to give way during fires as compared with metal of equal load-bearing strength is being brought to public attention. Wood-paper laminates are upgrading wood for siding and plywood; veneer reinforced paperboard boxes are far stiffer than standard paperboard. Many other new developments are on the horizon to widen the market for wood. In addition to the expanding population, the urge of many people of moderate means to have a vacation home in addition to their year-round urban residence will mean greater use of lumber.

Public and Corporate Competition

The forest owner is in competition with both corporate and public forest holdings. As of 1963, the commercial forest lands of the United States were held as follows:[5]

	acres (rounded)
National forests	97,000,000
Other federal, state, and county forests	45,000,000
Forest industries	67,000,000
Farm forests	151,000,000
Other private	149,000,000

As timber and other tree products are marketed from both public and corporate forest lands, the private forest owner is, in essence, in competition with both. In many areas of the West, the national forest holdings are sufficiently large to form a major source of timber supply; the federal stumpage offered for sale at public bid tends to control the market. Corporate holdings are extensive in Maine and certain areas of the South and West. Since most corporate owners are companies engaged in the lumber or paper industry, they have a market for their forest products. These same corporations may also purchase standing timber, logs, and pulpwood from other owners, allowing their own holdings to serve as insurance against future shortages.

Neither the government nor corporations are offering standing timber for sale at distressed prices. The same cannot be said for the some three million owners of small holdings. It is such owners, many of whom feel that they must cut their timber whenever merchantable, who keep pulpwood stumpage prices at a low level in most areas. Because these owners tend to degrade the quality as well as the quantity of their timber supply, they offer limited competition in the quality timber market. They are, however, at present, so numerous and many so needy that few buyers need bid high for their timber.

Various efforts have been made by extension foresters and other public foresters to stimulate group action by forest owners to improve their competitive position. Forest cooperatives were tried during the thirties and forties, but most terminated business within a few years. One of the most extensive operations has been that of the New England Forestry Foundation, which offers forestry services to owners on a percentage fee basis. Connwood had a similar service for Connecticut owners. Other associations, including farmers' cooperatives, have also offered services in marketing timber. Various informal or neighbor cooperative ventures have also been of help, but for the most part individual owners of woodland have not joined or stayed with cooperative marketing associations.

Certain paper companies and other forest product manufacturing firms in the South offer a marketing and management service to forest owners. When these services are available, the forest owner might well investigate using them; the programs tend to assure good management of the land for the owner and a preferred market for his timber in return for his keeping his land in good growing condition. Few companies ask for exclusive timber rights in return for such services, feeling that their own company can meet competitive prices in its area of operation.

Stumpage Prices

Stumpage prices, those for trees standing in the forest, vary widely by location, timber volume, accessibility, and species of trees. Pulpwood stumpage in the Northeast brought $1.50 to $2.50 per cord for hardwood and pine, and $4.00 to $8.00 for spruce, during the period 1960-67. Southern prices for pine and hardwood were about double the corresponding Northeastern prices.

The gross income that could normally be expected in the Northeast from growing hardwood pulpwood would, therefore, be in the neighborhood of $1.00 to $2.00 per acre per year and of sawtimber, $2.00 to $5.00 per acre per year. Because of better markets and more rapid growth rates, the owner in the southeastern states may anticipate a yearly income of double these amounts. Quality has little effect on pulpwood prices because of the abundance of supply in proportion to the needs of the mills.

The market for fuelwood, posts, poles, rustic fencing, and novelties is local and limited, and the sale of these products can be expected to bring in barely enough income to cover taxes and management costs. Sawtimber, on the other hand, can bring in from $2.00 to $5.00 per acre per year gross on lands that are only moderately productive and up to $15.00 to $20.00 for lands well stocked with high-quality, rapidly growing trees of merchantable size.

The price range, by species, of standing trees shows wide variation. In 1965 the ranges reported for New York State were as shown in Table 1.

TABLE 1
THE PRICE RANGE OF STANDING TIMBER

Species	Sawtimber stumpage Per MBF Doyle Scale*
Beech	$ 8 - 25
Birch	20 - 65
Hard maple	20 - 70
Soft maple	10 - 55
Ash	15 - 75
Basswood	10 - 50
Black cherry	20 - 100
Elm	10 - 35
Red oak	10 - 40
White pine	10 - 25
Hemlock	5 - 30
Spruce	10 - 25

*Per thousand board feet of logs as scaled by the Doyle Log Rule. See Chapter VI, pp. 138-39, for explanation of log rules.

This extremely wide range in price indicates that many factors go into determining the value of standing timber.

Certainly species, quality of timber, accessibility and ease of logging are important, but even more important is the presence of established industries prepared to pay a good price for quality timber. The forest owner can well afford to seek out such markets. He may be able to help his logger get higher prices, and in turn, some of this gain may be returned to him in increased stumpage price. By making special arrangements with operators of veneer mills, wood-turning establishments, manufacturers of furniture stock, handle factories, and even pulpwood buyers the owner may build for himself a favored market position. Information on prices, to be meaningful, must be obtained currently from local foresters and timber buyers.

Financial Review

At this stage the reader may wish to set down some cost and

TABLE 2

COST AND RETURN FIGURES FOR FOREST PROPERTY

Capital investment:		
Land (500 acres @ $20)	$10,000	
Acquisition costs (@ $3 per acre)	1,500	
Equipment	100	
Initial capital investment		$11,600
Annual income:		
Timber growth (@ $2 per acre), unrealized	$ 1,000	
Family recreation, e.g.	250	
Total income		$ 1,250
Annual operating costs:		
Supplies . . . . $ 25		
Taxes (@ $.50 per acre) 250		
Management (@ $.50 per acre) 250		
Total annual operating costs . . . . $ 525		
Interest (@ 5 per cent) 580		
Total cost		1,105
Net profit	$ 145	

return figures to see what he could be getting himself into by buying a forest property. He might sum it up in the manner indicated in Table 2.

If he sold no timber there would be no realized income; hence the loss deductible from personal income for tax purposes would be $525. Assuming him to be liable for federal and state income taxes in the 40 per cent bracket, he would realize a tax savings of $260. The return on his investment would then be as is shown in Table 3.

TABLE 3
RETURN ON INVESTMENT

Interest	$580
Tax saving	260
Net profit	145
Total	$985

This is the equivalent of 8.4 per cent on his investment.

At this point his wife might point out that he would have an investment of $11,600 and an annual net outlay of $525, from which his only current return is an income tax deduction of $260. Moreover, the outlay may continue for a decade before a substantial sale of timber brings in offsetting returns. He may, therefore, wish to re-explore ways to reduce his costs or to share them with others.

First, he must not pay too much for his land, or at least for those components which he expects to be self-supporting. With annual growth from a forest property during the development period valued at no more than $1.00 to $5.00 per acre and expenses of $1.00 per acre, investment in land should be but $10.00 to $25.00 per acre. Much land may be bought within this price range. There are sections of the country where forest land prices are considerably higher; here the owner must look for compensating factors to operate, such as more rapid timber growth, higher stumpage prices, or alternate sources of income to justify the higher land prices. Otherwise, an appropriate portion of the higher land price will have to be charged against individual satisfactions and intangible values in recreational use, or speculation that future land prices will be higher.

An ideal way to finance a forest estate is to make a favorable purchase of desirable forest land containing a substantial volume of timber of merchantable size. In the unusual case, where this may be possible, the owner may harvest part of the timber to reduce capital investment, support investment in additional properties, or to pay off an acquisition loan. Several foresters have used this means of building up substantial private timber holdings. Most of those who have invested in forest lands, however, have acquired young timber and been obliged to go through a long, lean period while awaiting its growth to merchantable size. Land supporting timber that is not yet merchantable but is growing vigorously into small sawlog size may prove to be the most favorable purchase from this standpoint. Usually initial cost is much lower, and percentage growth rate is higher than for timber already merchantable.

Even on lands cut over within the past decade or two, some timber sales may be possible without significant reduction of future timber growth. If tree marking is directed toward harvesting low-quality trees to make way for better ones, or thinning over-dense stands, the reduction in value of growth may be negligible; in fact, most properties will contain some coarse, limby trees passed over in earlier cuttings that may now be merchantable. The removal of these will benefit the remaining stand, and the earlier this is done the better it will be for future income.

Associations

An association of timberland owners to pool interests and bargaining power may prove feasible and effective. Such an organization is also another way of improving the liquidity of a forest investment because it strengthens timber markets and makes forest ownership more attractive for others in the neigh-

A forest buyer searches for land bearing good stands of young sawtimber. What he most often finds is cutover lands with unwanted residuals. Still, even these trees will become merchantable as better timber grows more scarce.

borhood. A forest estate owner might, for his own protection and good, encourage others to acquire forest land for investment purposes in nearby communities. If a composite property from several owners can be built up to a combined area of five thousand acres or more, the landowners may be in a position to retain a consulting forester, to employ a custodian, and to bargain collectively with timber operators on sale of stumpage. Landowner associations have proved quite successful in Scandinavia, Japan, and Germany in improving the prices for stumpage from members' woodlands and in making possible technical and other services. These may be organized along cooperative lines, or as corporations, or simply as loose associations. The more informal type of association will probably suffice until the group gains sufficient size and strength to employ a part-time manager.

One such association in the Black Forest of Germany has been operating for several decades. The members have built up for their association a reputation for delivering timber of superior quality for which they receive a price advantage. They manage their forest stands to grow this high-quality product. Forest owner associations in Scandinavia have considerable economic and political power that enables them to bargain successfully with timber buyers, representatives of forest labor, and also with local tax assessors. Such associations may be able also to provide a line of credit to member owners of forest estates.

The potential for obtaining financial resources through an association goes even further. For example, a group of five or more families might elect to go together and purchase a property of some one thousand or more acres. This could be divided so that each owner would have his share of the total and each could erect his own camp or summer home. A real opportunity for development financing exists here, moreover, in that such an association, if formally organized, can apply for federal financial aid under the U.S. Food and Agriculture acts of 1962 and 1965. Funds borrowed under the provisions of these acts may be used for constructing water and sewage disposal systems, and even for the construction of recreational facilities that might be jointly used by the families.

Eventually, an association might grow to include several families, making it possible to construct and share swimming pools, bridle trails, tennis courts, a golf course, and various other recreational facilities. Federal loans that may be available can carry a large percentage of the developmental costs; furthermore, these loans may be paid off over a long period of time at reasonable interest rates. The association could thereby enjoy some of the advantages of village living, with telephone, water, sewage, and electrical services and with shared recreational opportunities, while holding and controlling for individual or association use a substantial area of forest land capable of providing hunting, fishing, riding, and other recreational opportunities. The economies of joint management of the entire holding and joint sharing of custodial fees and other services has much to commend it. Also, village-type living makes possible relying on neighbors for emergency transportation and other help and prevents the isolation that occurs when one family lives remotely from others. It has much to commend it for summer use by the family when the worker must be away during the week but can return to the summer retreat for his weekends.

Various related condominium arrangements for supplying particular modern living needs of Americans are growing rapidly. Second homes, as recreational retreats, retirement residences or family "conditioners," are rising at the rate of 100,000 a year. Their locations are usually centered around desirable environmental settings or scenic attributes which all participants wish to maintain, frequently with extensive forest ownership which the joint or participating owners develop to meet their own asset goals.

Direct Public Financial Aid

The U.S. Department of Agriculture, during the past decades, has offered a number of financial incentives to farmers to carry out forestry and other conservation measures on their lands. These are provided by various legislative acts administered by the Soil Conservation Service (SCS), the Agricultural Stabilization and Conservation Service (ASCS), the Farmers Home Administration (FHA), and other agencies. These laws were enacted to aid the farmer in making a more satisfactory living from his land; their aim is not to increase agricultural crop production but, rather, to limit it by assisting in the constructive retirement of land from cultivation. Some of their programs have provided money for forest planting and the planting of cover for game, for various water conservation measures including construction of farm ponds, and for land terracing and other soil-conserving measures. Limited funds have been made available for improving farm woodlands. Such benefits available to individuals were considerably extended under the Food and Agriculture acts of 1962 and 1965. These laws also provide authority for loans to farmers to convert farms into commercial recreational enterprises. Loans are available for constructing campgrounds, picnic areas, swimming areas, cabins for summer use, and related recreational purposes. The law provides that loans up to $60,000 may be made available for construction, with additional amounts up to $30,000 for operating expenses. They are repayable over a period of thirty and twenty years, respectively.

Neither these loans nor the various financial aids provided under the Agricultural Conservation Program have been strictly designed to aid the forest owner, as such, but rather the farmer. However, a number of the provisions may be available to other owners of rural land. From time to time, various bills have been considered by the Congress that would provide direct financial aid to the forest owner for timber production activities, but none have passed. First, the laws would be difficult to administer; second, they have generally been opposed by the forest products industries for various reasons. One is the fear that they might lead to the government acquiring such lands through default on loan repayment. Also, they express concern that financial aids to owners would tend to place an inflated price on forest lands beyond what they otherwise would command. This would make possible the perpetuation, at least for a time, of uneconomic-sized units and financially weak owners. Many have felt that it is better that these lands be lowered in price so that they can be acquired and built up into productive-sized holdings by individuals or corporations with adequate financial strength to provide good management. Financial aids to forest owners have been sought vigorously by neither the forest owners nor the U.S. Forest Service. Actually, the forest owners have not been organized nationally to make their wishes felt in the Congress to the extent that farmers have, nor have they been recognized as individuals in need of financial assistance to the extent that farmers have been.

Forest Tax Laws

In addition to the usual land and school tax structures, a number of states have laws that provide for special assessment or deferred taxing of forest lands. Some of these impose a yield tax when the timber is harvested. Other states may have no yield tax but instead require that the land be appraised at the time it is entered under their forest tax law and be reappraised when withdrawn. The state then imposes a tax on the increase in land value during the interval it has been under the tax law. This imposes little hardship on an owner as long as he continues to own the land. If he sells, however, it does impose a heavy tax if land values increase owing to favorable location, the growth of nearby industry, population increase, or simply inflationary trends over a long period of time. The latter, alone, might increase land values so as to impose a highly burdensome tax under such a law. In one state the tax was levied at 100 per cent of the increased value.

The yield taxes, if no more than 6 to 10 per cent, are usually lower than the annual tax on the land. The difficulty here is that a bare land tax is often continued, in any case, and this can be quite high so that the yield tax tends to become simply an additional cost to the landowner. If the property is well stocked with timber that is already of merchantable size, the annual land tax, unless excessive, imposes no great burden and may, in fact, be considerably lower than the yield tax will become provided the owner is successful in building up the productivity of his property. Careful investigation should be made to determine if actual benefits are in line with expectations before committing land to tax deferral measures.

A recent approach to rural land taxing has an especial appeal to forest owners. This is to assess the land for taxation on the basis of current use rather than market value. The rationale back of this proposal is that open land, either in farm or forest, is in itself a pleasing sight near metropolitan areas. Moreover, keeping some such land in sizable tracts free from subdivision and so-called development reserves it for the future needs of parks, schools, and other public or industrial organizations. To attach speculative values to such lands inevitably drives them out of use for farming or timber growing. One of the attractive features of most European cities is the freedom of fringe blight between city and countryside that characterizes almost every city of the United States. States that have enacted such assessment measures are Maryland, Connecticut, Maine, and Florida.

The Florida law has been written with the needs of the forest owner given special consideration. Pine lands, for example, are classified on the basis of timber growth potential as revealed by soil surveys. A stumpage value is assigned to the growth, and from this value is subtracted $1.50 as the estimated cost, other than property taxes, of managing forest lands. The remainder, capitalized at 7 per cent, is the assessed valuation. For example, if the owner had land capable of growing one cord per acre per year with an assigned stumpage value of $3.25 per cord, the calculation would be:

$3.25--$1.50 = $ 1.75 net to be capitalized

$$\frac{\$1.75}{\$0.07} = \$25.00 \text{ assessed valuation}$$

Such a law recognizes three things:

1) Forest land taxes should be based on the productivity of the land for timber crops.

2) Basic management costs must be met in addition to taxes.

3) A reasonably attractive interest rate is justifiable in view of the public services forests provide that do not accrue to the landowner, and of the risks in forest ownership from natural hazards and fluctuating markets.

Such a law could be a real boon to forest owners in states where taxes bear little or no relationship to the timber growth potential of the land.

Private Loans

Federal land banks and commercial banks do make loans on rural lands. These are mortgaged loans repayable over a period of up to twenty years and usually cover all improvements as well as the forest, itself. They usually have restrictions against cutting unless an appropriate reduction in the loans is made at the time of timber harvest. These, on the whole, are probably the most satisfactory for an individual forest owner, provided he can look forward with confidence to the necessary capital funds for liquidating the loan. He must recognize, however, that annual repayments of principal are usually required and that he will be obliged to make these payments in addition to interest from his total income sources, whatever these may be. Since timber values fluctuate rather widely, such loans are normally restricted to no more than one-half the current market value of the timber. Where the timber on the property has recently been cut over, such loans, if obtainable, would be so low as to be of little aid to the owner.

Because timber growth rates are generally no more than 10 per cent per year, and often much less than this, and since the mortgaged loans are generally restricted to one-half the value of the timber, it is difficult to build up a forest property through mortgage loans with any assurance that at loan maturity the individual, rather than the bank, will have ownership of the property. The forest landowner, therefore, is counseled to look largely to his personal capital and income as a means of financing his forest holding, or to the possibility of organizing an association among friends and acquaintances interested in a like venture. Even then, it might be better to provide for association ownership rather than dividing a large holding into individual parcels because of greater efficiencies of management, and because of the high degree of variability of soil and timber growth on different portions of the area and the difficulty in judging such variations.

Operating a Business or Leasing

The prospective owner who is unable to obtain sufficient financing for his property personally, or through any of the possibilities mentioned above, may be obliged to look to operating some portion of it as a subsidiary business, at least for a decade or more, or leasing a part or all of his use of the property to others. Of the various possibilities, probably leasing hunting rights will cause the least interference with personal use and management, provided the owner, himself, is not a hunter. Such a lease may later be terminated when the income therefrom is no longer necessary. After all, the hunting season is relatively short and, except for deer hunting, offers little hazard to other users.

Leasing land to acquaintances for summer campsites may also work out, particularly if a stream or pond is available for the use of the campers. Some services and facilities must usually be provided in this case, and if the property is small, the choice sites may have to be given up to lessees rather than be reserved for family use. Leasing for summer homesites is a step toward alienation of a portion of the property and should be avoided. It might in this case be better to make an outright sale of the site, particularly where such sites can be restricted to a portion of the property where resident use does not interfere with the major objectives of forest ownership.

Attempts to set up a separate business, such as fee camping or fee rental for picnicking and other purposes, usually impose burdens the absentee owner cannot meet personally. His best alternatives here would probably be to lease such a concession to someone else, either for a specific sum or a share in income. This is probably the least desirable way to obtain necessary financing, and if it is the only alternative to giving up the idea of owning a forest, the latter may be the wiser course to follow.

Summary

Forests produce wood, water, wildlife, forage, and recreation. The two products likely to be of most value to the average forest owner are wood and personal recreation. Such minor products as Christmas trees and greens, ferns, edible fruits and nuts, pharmaceutical products, and other specialty materials may have a local market and, if so, the owner should investigate the potential. Maple syrup, fuelwood, pulpwood, and leasing of hunting rights may bring in some additional income but are unlikely to cover much more than property taxes and management costs. Sawtimber, piling, and veneer logs, considered on a nationwide basis, offer the best potential market for the estate owner. Income during the first decade of operation is likely to be no more than enough to cover management costs and taxes if the forest property is made up mostly of young timber stands below merchantable size. Thereafter, income should exceed costs by a margin sufficient to pay a fair return for interest and risk on the investment to date. Much will depend upon the skill and astuteness of the owner in acquiring suitable land initially and in seeking lucrative markets for the products of his forest. The long-term market outlook for wood, including lumber, need not be viewed with any pessimism.

Forestry, being an extensive rather than intensive use of land, brings in relatively low income per acre. This means that holdings should be five hundred acres or larger. To be financially successful, the forest owner should keep capital and operating costs low. He must have patience and learn to use time as an investment asset, as well as money and skill.

Cost-sharing opportunities exist through leasing fishing and hunting rights, forming a partnership or club with shared benefits, or developing an association or condominium eligible for financial assistance under the Food and Agriculture acts of 1962 and 1965, and other lines of credit. He may also charge some of the expense to personal and family recreation.

Land bearing sufficient merchantable timber to permit sales adequate to cover all costs is difficult to find and expensive to purchase, but when it is available it should not be over-looked.

Opportunities for direct federal financial assistance to the individual forest owner, unless he is a bona fide farmer, are limited, and funds from government agencies should not be relied upon as a major source of financing for purchase or meeting costs.

Various tax deferral laws have been passed in the several states, but none has proved to be wholly satisfactory to either the local taxing authorities or the forest owners. The general property tax seems to be returning to favor, and it serves both local government and owners well, provided it is properly administered. The recent development of assessing lands on the basis of use, rather than at full market value, has its appeal to the forest owner as well as to the farmer. It has the advantage to the public of making possible the retention in agricultural and forest use of land near urban centers.

Forest owners should use private sources of credit with circumspection because of the relatively slow rate of timber growth and the fluctuations in markets for products. Personal financial resources should generally be used, and if these are inadequate, it may be best to seek other investments.

Carefully planned investments in forest properties have paid off handsomely in the past. It seems likely that opportunities to make similar successful investments are as bright today as at any time in the past. Success depends on doing far better than the average, and this means paying careful attention to all aspects of the forest investment.

The owner should not overlook as one of the greatest returns the personal perquisites and satisfactions of forest ownership.

LITERATURE CITED

1. J. A. Cope, *Maple Sirup and Sugar,* Cornell *Extension Bulletin 397* (Ithaca, N.Y., 1949), 32.

2. Helen Nearing and Scott Nearing, *The Maple Sugar Book* (New York: John Day Co., 1950), 271.

3. A. M. Sowder, "Christmas Trees—The Industry," *Trees (The Yearbook of Agriculture)* (Washington, D.C.: U.S. Department of Agriculture, 1949), 248-51.

4. Charles H. Stoddard, *The Small Private Forest in the United States* (Washington, D.C.: Resources for the Future, Inc., 1961), 171.

5. U.S. Department of Agriculture, Forest Service, *Timber Trends in the United States,* Forest Resource *Report No. 17* (Washington, D.C., 1965), 235.

6. F. E. Winch, Jr., *The Selection, Identification and Care of Your Christmas Tree and Greens,* Cornell *Extension Bulletin 983* (Ithaca, N.Y., 1957).

III

Selecting a Site for the Forest Property

Commercial forest lands within easy motoring distance of cities exist throughout the United States, except for the Prairie Plains region and the Great Basin. Some regions, however, are, greatly preferable to others from an investor's viewpoint. Generally favorable are the southern states from Virginia to Florida and west to Oklahoma and eastern Texas; the northeastern and Lake States extending south to Maryland and Missouri; the northern Rocky Mountains and the West Coast. Within broad regional areas localities with active timber industries, good soils, abundant rainfall, and gentle topography are to be favored.

Timber growth possibilities vary widely according to the region, soil, and individual property. Very poor conditions are likely to prevail in high mountain regions such as the Adirondacks and Catskills, the White Mountains, parts of the southern Appalachians, and in the high western mountains. The eastern foothills, on the other hand, may be highly productive. Deep, fertile, well-watered soil with a favorable climate is conducive to rapid tree growth. Softwoods (conifers)—pines, hemlock, Douglas fir, spruce, and fir—tend to give higher volume yields and in some areas to be in higher demand than hardwoods (broad-leafed trees). However, hardwoods of high quality and preferred species bring top prices and may grow at a gratifying rate. Hardwood lands are much more abundant throughout the East and South than those supporting coniferous trees. General information may be had from a book on regional silviculture.[1] Potentially profitable personal forest holdings can be located in the East from Maine to Florida and west beyond the Mississippi to the Great Plains. They can also be found among the West Coast forests.

Information on the productivity of lands throughout New York State is available in the bulletin on growth rates by Ferree and Hagar.[3] Information on the general conditions and markets for forest products in New York State can be obtained from the publication by Stout, *Atlas of Forestry.*[4] The prospective landowner in New York would do well to study both these publications before deciding on a general area in which to look for a forest property. Similar information may be had for other states. Information on soil productivity is available from soil surveys made by the U.S. Soil Conservation Service and other agricultural agencies. Local county agricultural extension agents will have the information needed.

Industrial Climate

Equally as important as timber growth and quality to the property owner concerned with income on investment is the industrial climate of the state or region. This includes such considerations as local use and markets for forest products, whether industries are expanding or barely holding their own, abundance or scarcity of woods labor, the effectiveness of organizations of woods workers, workmen's compensation insurance rates, the strength of organizations for woodland owners, the attitude of state government toward private forest ownership, taxation of forest property, regulation of timber cutting on private lands, and general social costs imposed upon industries. Use of, and markets for, wood products are related closely to population, the states with the highest populations—New York, California, and Pennsylvania—being the top wood users.

The industrial climate for forest products industries has generally been favorable in Maine, the South generally, and the West Coast. In these areas the pulp and paper and veneer and plywood industries are expanding rapidly, and markets for standing timber are good to excellent. It is not mere chance that it is in the South and on the West Coast also that timber growth is rapid, stumpage prices offered owners are more realistic in terms of costs of growing timber, and services available to landowners by industries are the most widespread. Nor should it be surprising that here forest land prices are high. Unfortunately, not all aspirant forest owners live in the South or on the West Coast.

Woods laborers are attracted to areas where they are in demand, and labor, therefore, is abundant in the regions where timber industries are most aggressive—the South and the West Coast. The northeastern states have been able to look to Quebec for much of their woods labor. Logging operations are most highly mechanized on the West Coast; here woods labor is most productive, more highly paid, and better organized. Mechanization, for the type of timber to be handled, is well developed in the South but less so in the north central states and Northeast, exclusive of Maine. The higher pulpwood stumpage prices paid in the South relative to the North is due, in part, to lower logging costs in the South, but the cost of wood delivered to the mill tends to be much the same in the North and South.

Workmen's compensation for injury on the job is a universal requirement; the generosity of courts, however, varies considerably from one state to another. To protect both workers and employers, workmen's compensation insurance may be purchased from underwriters, whose rates vary widely from state to state, ranging upward from a low of $5.00 per $100.00 of payroll for logging and sawmill workers. New York State's rates have been among the highest—in excess of $20.00 per $100.00 of payroll. This has unquestionably been a deterrent to the development of the primary forest industries generally in New York State as well as to the formation and operation of logging companies. It has led to a plethora of one- and two-man logging operations. Such small enterprises, if set up as a partnership, are not required to carry compensation insurance on themselves, but if one of the loggers is injured in logging a forest owner's property, the property owner himself may be held liable. State compensation boards are set up to protect workmen, not landowners or industries. For this reason alone, the New York resident might consider developing forest holdings in Canada, Vermont, or Pennsylvania rather than in New York, or taking strong steps to be certain always of his own insurance protection.

The irony of the situation is that high compensation insurance rates discourage the kind of logging that is essential to promote efficiency and safety. Where effective safety measures have been vigorously promoted by industry and the public agencies, as in Quebec, the severity of individual accidents has lessened and the accident rate has declined sharply. Still, for the United States as a whole, logging has the highest accident rate and highest accident severity of all industries. The encouraging thing to keep in mind is that great improvements are possible.

Organizations of forest owners exist in a number of states. One providing the most effective service to owners is the New England Forestry Foundation, which operates throughout the New England states. The New York Forest Owners Association has been able to supply considerable current information of value to owners. Strong organizations also exist in the southern states. State forestry associations, though open to all laymen, also seek to help the owner. The American Forest Products Industries, of Washington, D.C., sponsor of well-managed private forests, which it will certify as Tree Farms, has been especially helpful to owners and can provide detailed information on associations in the various states. State foresters also will have such information.

Attitudes of the several states toward the private forest

owner are favorable throughout, but some state governments go much further than others to be helpful. Information on specific help provided by the state forester can be obtained by writing to him. Aside from protecting forest lands against fire, insects, and disease organisms, the states provide a number of services to individual owners, including distribution of tree planting stock and assistance in making timber sales.

It has been mentioned that many states have laws that provide for special tax considerations to forest landowners. The most effective approach appears to be that used in Florida, where the law relates assessed value to the productivity of the land for timber growing. The prospective owner can get information from state foresters and other appropriate officers on laws currently applicable in his own state.

Laws regulating the cutting of timber on private forest lands have been enacted by seventeen states. The statutes vary widely in requirements and stringency from state to state. None of the enactments are intended to discourage the owner interested in responsible management of his property, though some may tend to have that effect.

A compendium of forest laws prepared by Henry W. Falk in 1958 can serve as a useful reference.[2] For up-to-date information on specific points, a lawyer or the attorney in the state conservation department should be consulted. State departments of commerce can supply information on the condition of forest industries and their outlook for the future in particular regions.

Availability of Property to Acquire

As mentioned earlier, wide shifts in land ownership are now taking place throughout the United States, especially in the older settled regions where agriculture is no longer competitive with the rich, level, fertile lands of the Middle West. Generally speaking, hill lands and plateau lands above 1,200 feet elevation in the northern sections of the country are going out of agriculture. Some information on such trends can be obtained from studying successive census information on land area in farms, by counties. More up-to-date information can probably be gained by talking with local county agricultural agents or with agricultural economists at the state agricultural colleges. These people, generally well informed on the status of agriculture throughout the state, can usually furnish suggestions concerning areas that are worth examining. Forest management faculty members at the state forestry college are well-informed sources of guidance. The state forester's office is generally informed also and would be quite willing to cooperate in suggesting areas for consideration. Some help may be obtained from local newspapers in studying classified advertisements of land for sale, though these can prove misleading. Real estate agents may have rural listings, which, if found interesting, should be cross-checked with the county agricultural agent or local officer of the state forestry agency. Consulting foresters also can be engaged to canvass forest land purchase opportunities that meet defined interests of clients. It is their business to keep well informed on forestry opportunities in their area of operation.

Strictly forest lands, especially those of two hundred acres or less in size, tend to change hands rapidly, often just after the timber has been cut. Small sawmill operators or loggers, who do not care to have their capital tied up in land, tend to sell it after completing their logging operations. Lands also come on the market to close estates or because the owner is no longer able to work the land and needs money for living expenses or other purposes. Timber brokers may be found, but these are much fewer in numbers today than they were some three decades ago. A few agencies and some magazines have listings of large estate properties that may include forest lands. Usually the improvements are featured in this case, rather than forest land as such.

Selecting a Center of Operations

Having decided on major objectives and their priorities,

size of property, and amount to be invested, the prospective buyer's next important step is to find an area in which to acquire land permitting the realization of his objectives. One should expect to spend considerable time on this search and not be disappointed if in the process he may be obliged to make minor adjustments among objectives, for rarely does one find a property that meets all one's desires.

A forest holding should be located within two to three hours' travel time of one's home if it is to be used conveniently for weekends. With modern highways and airports, this may permit a radius of up to two hundred miles in which to search for a property. Obviously, the property should also be one that appeals to the individual personally, that has attractive attributes, potential for developing his ideas, views and vistas, challenging hiking points, the desired recreational features, and that offers in a nearby community the type of services one may need if his family is to spend much time on the property. It is well to start, first, with the state forester, state college of forestry, and state agricultural extension service for suggestions on counties to look over. If aware of an owner's objectives, these professionals may be able to offer advice that will allow him to limit his search to the most likely areas. Within counties, state district forest officers and county agricultural extension agents can be of great help; in fact, a visit with them may save miles of traveling back roads in search of likely areas.

Days spent searching for a center of operations appealing to the entire family will be time well spent. If these days are well spent, they may, in fact be looked back upon as one of the more enjoyable and profitable parts of the forest estate experience. The children will be alert for lakes, streams, ponds, mountains and other recreational attractions, while the mother will be thinking of food markets, laundromats, doctors, and hospitals. The father, meanwhile, should be seeking information on available properties, competing buyers, markets for forest products, resale possibilities, tax rates, and accessibility to home. He would be wise also to inquire about the attitudes of local people toward forest property ownership.

If he selects as a center of operations an area that attracts people with interests similar to his own, there will be social and, perhaps, economic advantages of significance. Also, such a center offers an opportunity to join with friends in an association that can lower land operating costs and increase the market for sale of products.

An outsider purchasing considerable areas of land in a settled community is certain to stimulate speculation in the minds of those who dwell there. Forest management is not yet a widely practiced business, and purchases may arouse suspicion that hidden motives exist that might be prejudicial to local interests. It may be well to inform tax assessors, real estate dealers, and other important local people of one's objectives once an acquisition program is started. Land ownership for long-term forestry does not ordinarily present the type of values that would tend to raise land prices appreciably. Most local people will react favorably toward an honest effort to improve the productivity of land and to make fuller use of assets that will make a continuing contribution to the welfare of the local community.

Markets for Products

Although good soil and high-value timber products are desirable, a good nearby market is even more important to financial success. Diversified markets are to be desired: Forests produce wood of a variety of sizes, shapes, and kinds. If markets for fuelwood, pulpwood, sawtimber, and veneer all are present, the landowner has a wide choice of products he may sell. He can realize returns from small-sized material and have an opportunity to weed out the ill-formed trees in early cuttings, thus improving the quality of subsequent forest growth. And it is through building up a forest of trees of high

Even an unimpressive sawmill may furnish a satisfactory market for logs of small size and medium quality. Unloading logs by hand is no task for the inexperienced.

timber quality that greatest returns may be realized. Time spent in sizing up market potential is likely to be well repaid, especially if the search results in finding mills operating near the property that use such specialty hardwood products as handle stock, baseball bat blanks, bowling pin stock, and spoolwood, as well as pulpwood, sawlogs, and veneer.

Possibilities of Resale

The uncertainties of life and fortune being what they are, properties having resale attraction are to be preferred to those lacking this advantage. Among items to consider here are accessibility to population centers, general popularity for vacationers, the nearness of established forest products industries and other land-holding organizations, possibilities of sale to public agencies for park and forest purposes, attractiveness for summer homes or other recreational development, and popularity of the area for other potential investors interested in landowning. Information on these matters can often be obtained from local bankers or real estate dealers. Some premium in price is certainly justified for properties having a ready resale.

Competition from Corporations for the Public

Many pulp and paper companies, and some lumber companies, have inaugurated forest land purchase programs since 1945. Companies such as these usually have well-defined purchase areas and confine their land purchases to them. Their holdings in an area may be a boon to the forest owner as well as furnishing competition. Corporations, which usually concentrate purchases on large, rather than small, properties, may be willing to exchange land to block up holdings. Their presence is generally evidence of a sustained market for wood products, and as long as they remain active in land purchasing, they provide a ready market for investors desiring to liquidate their holdings. Moreover, many large companies provide protection against fire beyond that afforded by public agencies, and some offer special forestry services to landowners. The owner of a modest-sized forest estate adjoining either corporate or publicly owned forest may often benefit from measures these large owners take to build roads, provide markets, and protect the forest against fire, insects, diseases, and trespass.

Neither corporations nor public forestry agencies wish to bid up the price of land. If a property has special appeal to the forest investor, he can usually outbid both corporate and public forest buyers, except for tracts suitable for park lands. Both, therefore, are to be viewed more as helpers than competitors.

Local Conveniences and Services

Not to be overlooked is the general attractiveness of the region and the availability of the services the family will need. If the property is to be a year-round residence, certainly a nearby shopping center, churches, schools, and good roads are important. Even a summer home should not be too far from stores, churches, and a general medical practitioner. The property owner occasionally will want to use the services of a title examiner and lawyer, a consultant forester, and a reliable timber operator. These are basic. Unless the investor has sufficient money to transform an area through his own activity, it is well to select a center of operations that has additional attractive features. Among these might be a golf club or country club; summer theater or music center; library and museum; a village that is, in itself, well kept, well designed, and attractive with overnight accommodations for friends or relatives who might overtax facilities on the property; and a local chamber of commerce or other civic group concerned with maintaining their village as a favorable place in which to do business and attractive to outsiders, including recreationists. Obviously, streams, lakes, and major land features tend to attract people. Good highways make it easy to reach one's property and, in turn, to find diverse markets for such salable materials as logs, poles for camps, fireplace wood, and cedar rails and posts for fencing and rustic construction. A local manager may be able to market a great many such products if a forest owner's lands are accessible to areas in which people are building summer homes. A final thing to keep in mind is commitment to the community; an owner of five hundred acres or more necessarily owes something to the community, especially if he lives on the land, and should expect to participate in local affairs. He should select a community that he can serve with pleasure.

Former Farmlands versus Uncleared Forest Lands

Virgin timberlands are now so scarce as to be virtually unavailable except in the far West. The buyer will have to choose from between two types of land—land once used for farming, and areas that have always been in forests. Either may be selected, but it is well to know what to look for in each case.

The release of land from agricultural use has been going on in the 1950's and 1960's at the rate of over 200,000 acres a year in New York State alone. Similar decline in farm holdings has occurred in New England, Pennsylvania, and throughout the South and Midwest; in fact, a great deal of farm decline occurred in New England and parts of the South before 1900. Lands that are hilly and have stony or poorly drained soils or soils that for other reasons are inherently low in productivity simply do not respond to modern mechanized agriculture. Hence, farming tends to be concentrated more and more on the better lands.

Neglected farms are often on the market. They may be purchased by another farmer to add to his holdings, by someone seeking a rural residence, or by others. Resale of poorer lands has been frequent in many areas, especially where local nonfarm employment opportunities diminish. Where two or more farms are combined for agricultural production, the owner may be willing to sell a part or all of his woodland.

The generally good roads that are to be found in most former agricultural areas in the Northeast and Midwest make such lands readily accessible to cities. Sizable acreages may be bought at prices that are generally not excessive in terms of the income of business and professional people.

When land changes from farmland to forest, a typical pattern may be observed. Sloping land erodes or cannot be machine tilled and eventually is used for hay crops. Pasturing to cattle follows. Unless mowed, eastern pastures soon become invaded by woody plants; hawthorn, red cedar, or juniper are early invaders because the thorns and prickly leaves protect these species against cows. Gradually these plants spread and are joined by wild apple and bush growth. As thickets form, pine and hardwood seedlings get started and grow up through the initial invaders. Fields abandoned without pasturing may be invaded directly by pine or various hardwoods. Often, this tree growth is made up of at least some species having potentially high value—white ash, sugar maple, black cherry in the Allegheny area, white pine and spruce in the Adirondacks and New England, sweet gum, tulip poplar, and southern pines in the southern Atlantic coastal plain and Carolina piedmont, aspen, pines and hardwoods in the Lake States. Lands that have been free from pasturing for twenty to thirty years and that have good stands of young sapling trees are well worth considering as a forest investment.

Such young regrowth always needs careful evaluation, however. Although from a distance the land may appear to be well covered with young trees, the stands need to be examined for species and quality. Many initial pioneer trees are short-lived species that will not produce sawtimber-sized logs. Examples are pin cherry, cedar, ironwood, choke cherry, sassafras, gray birch, and wild apple. Others may command only a low market price—aspen, elm, red maple, hickory, black gum, pin oak, balm of gilead. Even desirable species may be so open grown and limby as to have little commercial value. White pine can be badly damaged by weevil, red pine by shoot moth. The advice of a forester is needed, for only he can provide a well-informed opinion concerning the course of natural development toward a commercially valuable forest.

Even though the forester's report may be somewhat discouraging, the abandoned pastures and fields have their own appeal. Hawthorn, wild apple, Juneberry, dogwood, redbud, pin cherry, and elm make a showy appearance in the springtime when in flower. In the fall, sassafras, sweet gum, sumac, red maple, and aspen decorate the hillsides with rich autumnal colors. For the person seeking the amenities of rural life, this beauty may offer compensation for lower than normal financial returns. Also, old fields often offer good planting sites for conifers and for game food and cover plants.

By contrast, uncleared forest lands present much more of a residual of the past rigorous treatment that man has inflicted upon them. Almost invariably, these forested lands are on less accessible, less suitable, or more generally forested sites. Inspection may reveal a picked-over condition that has resulted because the more desirable species of commercial size have been removed periodically every decade or so over the past hundred years or more. Frequently, uncleared lands are purchasable because the owner has recently sold the merchantable timber and does not wish to carry the cut-over stand any longer. Such logged-over areas present a discouraging picture, but in relation to cost they may be a good investment if suitable conditions exist. Thickets of treetops, brush and briars, a few weak and damaged, unmerchantable, pole-sized trees bent by the wind, and scattered cull trees or unsalable species too branchy to have any utility—all these are typical of cut-over lots. Within five years after logging, an experienced forester can give a good estimate of future potentialities of such lands. By this time the tops have settled down, young seedlings and saplings are beginning to crowd out the briars, some of the residual pole trees will have responded by developing vigorous crowns, and the young thickets have encouraged the return of songbirds and provided a nutritious diet for deer. The owner has the satisfaction of seeing his forest become increasingly more inviting each year, and he may be gratified by the rate of growth of the young trees. While sixty slender hardwood poles, six inches or less in diameter, per acre may look rather lonesome right after cutting, they nevertheless have the potential to produce merchantable timber of value much more quickly than a tree plantation on a barren field.

One of the advantages of a forest area never cleared for tillage is that the desirable qualities of the forest soil have been little affected. The soil remains porous, with a good leaf litter, a vigorous soil fauna, and an uncompacted surface. Cultivated crops have not exhausted plant nutrients, nor has erosion stripped off the topsoil.

Cut-over lands, under some conditions, could be so low in recovery potential that they would be a poor investment at any price. Past loggers may not only have taken the best trees and left the poorest but also may have taken the best species of trees, leaving the unwanted, unmarketable ones. As a result, various undesirable species may take over the area like weeds in an untended garden and hold it for decades. To convert such a forest cover to a commercial stand may be more costly than to start with open fields.

Proximity of Large Properties

A center of operations should contain some fair-sized forest properties, two hundred acres or larger, one of which could serve as the key property. If only properties of forty acres or less are available, the acquisition of a five hundred acre or larger forest holding becomes an expensive and discouragingly slow operation. The buyer should have a choice of several such large properties to build up his holding. If properties of such size are not available, the buyer will probably

The cutover forest often has a few residual trees that attain commercial value along with pole-sized trees harvestable for pulpwood.

be better advised either to direct his attention to another region or to restrict his concept to one of Christmas tree growing or personal recreation rather than commercial timber production.

SUMMARY

Opportunities to purchase forest land appear to be fair to good in the eastern and southern states. Ownership patterns are shifting rapidly, and in this period of change the possibilities are better of building up a forest estate at prices that forest productivity would justify. The next twenty years may well see purchasing opportunities limited. Farms were still being given up during the 1960's, and this trend seems likely to continue for some time. Corporations in the timber business are active purchasers in many areas, but their presence need not discourage the individual buyer.

Buyers will need to consider industrial climate, including state forest and tax laws, vigor of wood-using industries, competition from other buyers, prospects of resale, and the availability of several properties of two hundred acres or more in selecting a center of operations.

A forest holding should be accessible to the owner for frequent use and enjoyment. It should be located near an attractive community affording essential services and markets for products and should be in a good timber-growing and marketing region. Proper sources should be consulted in selecting such a region.

LITERATURE CITED

1. John W. Barrett, ed., *Regional Silviculture of the United States* (New York: Ronald Press, 1962), 610.

2. Harry W. Falk, *Timber and Forest Products Law* (Berkeley, Calif.: Howell-North, 1958), 365.

3. Miles J. Ferree and Robert K. Hagar, *Timber Growth Rates for Natural Forest Stands in New York State,* State University of New York College of Forestry *Technical Publication 78* (Syracuse, N.Y., 1956), 56.

4. Neil J. Stout, *Atlas of Forestry in New York,* State University College of Forestry at Syracuse University *Bulletin No. 41* (Syracuse, N.Y., 1958), 95.

IV

Buying Forest Land

The aspirant forest property owner is ready to venture forth in search of properties to buy only after having taken the following steps:

1) clarified his motives for owning a forest and determined that these are consistent within themselves, and in harmony with family desires,

2) reviewed the costs involved and determined that these can be met without skimping on family needs,

3) located a center of operation that can meet his objectives,

4) found a suitable community to which he would be willing to make a personal commitment.

Land purchasing can be an absorbing and pleasurable experience.

Acquiring Small Holdings

The buyer will be obliged, in most cases, to build up his own property through successive small acquisitions; hence, he will need to know how to go about doing so. There are few large land holdings in the United States that are for sale that would make a suitable forest property holding—the feudal pattern of land holdings did not survive when transplanted to America. Moreover, few owners, so far, have attempted to build up large forest estates, and most of those who have done so still cherish them. These are not for sale. The necessity of acquiring small holdings offers both advantages and disadvantages. The advantages are that the prospective owner can pick and choose among the properties he will acquire and omit those that would be low in productivity or otherwise a burden to ownership. Since road systems are already developed, capital expenditures are less. Scattered parcels also are insurance against excessive damage from a single fire or tornado. The disadvantages are that several individual parcels must be acquired, each of which involves fairly costly examination, negotiation, and title clearance. Also, scattered, properties have considerable length of boundary to maintain; the cost, though minor, is one that increases the cost of custodianship. Roughly speaking, the costs of negotiation with the owner and of making a title examination bear little relationship to the size of property, except that large properties are more likely to have been surveyed and to have had an up-to-date title examination. Small properties may have very involved titles that are costly to search. The costs of examining the property on the ground, locating its boundaries, making a timber evaluation, checking on soil and general productivity, and making a boundary survey increase more in relationship to the perimeter of the property than to its area. Small properties are likely to have been parts of farms and may still be carried on the tax rolls as farm (cultivated) land rather than forest land, therefore carrying a correspondingly higher assessment. Studies in Maine indicate that small forest properties, in general, carried a higher assessment per acre than large ones. It is readily evident, therefore, that there are real savings to be had wherever a large property may be acquired as opposed to several small ones, provided the attributes sought are not compromised.

Locating the Key Property

Success in building up a forest holding may depend to a large degree upon locating a key property to acquire. This property preferably should be large enough to insure a successful venture even if others cannot be added to it. To start acquiring land in small parcels, especially if these are scattered, is likely to be both expensive and discouraging.

Large properties, even if available, are unlikely to meet all of the objectives of ownership. But the key property should meet the major objective, for it is around it that the estate will be built up. Good soil, favorable topography, timber of good quality and merchantable or near merchantable size are more important for an income-producing estate than that it have a summer dwelling or other recreational features. These can be sought in smaller properties located within a ten- to fifteen-mile driving radius. A forest estate is necessarily large, and motor transportation is essential in its management in any case. Thereby the owner grants himself flexibility in meeting minor objectives without hazard to his major interest.

The key property may have been located in the preliminary search for a center of operations. If so, it should be acquired as promptly as possible and additional acquisitions built around it. It is surprising how rapidly a property can be blocked up where land changes hands frequently.

Acquiring a place to live near the key property may be the next step. The dwelling should afford convenience but without diverting too much attention from building up the property. If an owner is looking forward to a place for retirement some ten to fifteen years hence, he might even consider using public accommodations or renting a summer home for a period while looking for the type of home he would wish to buy. There is much economy in time and energy, especially in winter, in stopping in a warm motel rather than digging a summer cottage out of the snow and making it livable for one or two nights while spending the days looking for new properties to acquire. The amount spent for rentals may turn out to be far less than taxes and upkeep on a second home that gets but limited use.

Time should not be lost in building up the estate to a size that will make it a good operating unit; yet, on the other hand, land purchasing cannot be hurried without paying the price for haste. Local custodians or real estate dealers, if they know what the buyer is looking for, can be of immense help in being alert for lands likely to come onto the market and notifying him promptly. Properties may then be examined and acquired at a satisfactory rate without the buyer being obliged to pay excessive prices.

Property examination should always precede purchase. In acquiring the key property as well as other land, special attention should be given to such features as accessibility, topography, soil, timber types, timber values, tax burden, and other carrying costs.

Accessibility

General accessibility has been covered under the selection of a center of operation. Individual property accessibility must also be examined. Preferably, a property should be located along a public highway or have stated in the deed that a right-of-way exists to it. A property located a half-mile or more from a motor road across lands of others, from whom the new property owner will have to acquire a right-of-way as well as build a road, would have to be a choice one, indeed, to justify this risk and expense. Many old roads exist in sections of the country settled relatively early, and some of these rights-of-way have been maintained and provide access, though they may require some considerable expenditure of effort to build an acceptable road. A good public road to, or through, the property may mean higher taxes, but these may be cheap compared with the cost of building and maintaining a private road.

Topography

Owners may have personal preferences for certain topographic features—a mountain, a trout stream, a lake—all will enhance the value of the property for personal and public recreation. The tax assessor will also be aware of this. Property on which a pond or small lake can be constructed at modest expense is more likely to be available than property that already contains a natural pond or lake. Water adds many satisfactions to the owner and his family. One must recognize that all of these features produce income in terms of personal satisfaction, though not necessarily in terms of cash to pay the taxes, custodial fees, and other carrying charges involved in owning forest lands. The mountain is likely to have thin, rocky soils that are low in productivity. The owner may decide it is smarter to depend upon public beaches, mountain trails, and other recreational features than to acquire his own. Those who want a lake or mountain for personal use should be prepared to pay the cost of ownership.

However careful the buyer may be, he is almost certain to acquire some acreage in swamp, ridge tops, rocky ledges, and open lands capable of adding but little to timber production. These must be accepted and used for whatever benefits they will yield at modest or no cost. Often they may be suitable for esthetic or recreational use.

Soils

The importance of selecting a site with good soil is paramount for an income-producing forest. Roads can be built, water courses dammed for ponds, and trees planted. The evidences of such improvements can be seen within decades, but soil building requires centuries.

The productivity of forest soils depends greatly upon their capacity to hold and release to the plant roots an ample supply of moisture, for only rarely does the soil lack the fertility for good tree growth. Sandy soils having a relatively high water table, some ten to thirteen inches below the surface, are excellent for growing pine and many hardwoods. The best tree growth, of course, occurs on deep fertile loam soils, but most of these, unless stony, are used for agriculture. Such soils are, however, found in the "coves," the lower valley slopes, in mountain areas, and in glacial moraines.

The forest owner is fortunate that his crops of timber,

wildlife, and water remove little fertility from the soil. Forest cover gradually adds to soil fertility; the annual leaf fall builds up the organic content in the soil, helping to retain moisture, and the humic acids induce chemical breakdown of soil minerals, thereby releasing potassium, phosphorous, and other plant nutrient elements. The cost of applying fertilizers to correct poor soil conditions is generally far beyond the cost of acquiring a better forest property in the beginning.

John Preston, in his book *Developing Farm Woodlands,*[1] discusses the ideal soil conditions for hardwoods. The soil should be loose and crumbly, and the annual litter deposit should be undisturbed, with the soil beneath it moist. Although pine stands commonly occupy drier sites, the litter should be present and functioning. In general, a loose, moist, well-drained soil with a six- to eight-inch layer of topsoil is high in productivity.

Soil texture, which is determined by the size of the soil grains, is a general guide to productivity. The organic matter in a soil is composed of leaves and twigs and the soil organisms responsible for their decay. Earthworms, mites, insects, and other creatures burrow through the soil creating channels for air, root, and water penetration and converting the nutrients stored in the litter to forms that can be reused by plants.

In looking at the soil, three other observations should be made—for evidences of fire damage, grazing, and soil erosion.

Fire damages the forest by destroying seedlings and organic matter and injures trees that have thin bark. Charred stumps and fire scars on fallen logs as well as on standing trees are indicators of an earlier fire. The height, width, and depth of a fire scar on a standing tree is an indicator of the intensity of the fire. A severe fire, especially where there has been an accumulation of leaf litter, may consume the organic matter in the topsoil and kill the soil-dwelling organisms. Where this has occurred, several decades have been known to elapse before a good forest cover returns; in fact, forest lands have been converted to worthless grass, ferns, and shrubs by such fires.

Light fires, on the other hand, may cause little damage. In the South prescribed burning serves as an aid to forestry. The practice reduces the accumulated fuel, prepares seed beds for conifers, and may curtail brown spot disease of longleaf pine needles.

If a forest or woodlot looks like a park, this is probably because it has been grazed by cattle. Domestic animals grazing a woodlot are often more destructive than a fire. They consume and kill out the naturally occurring forest herbs, making way for grass that tends to exclude tree seedlings. They browse on seedlings, deforming them, and injure the branches and bark of saplings. Their hooves may kill surface feeding roots and injure others so that fungal growth gets started.

Soil erosion may result from fire, poor logging practice, or poorly constructed roads. If erosion is widespread and not already arrested by vegetation, the land so affected will probably be a financial burden to the owner and an eyesore on his property.

Forest Types

The selection of an area in which to own forest land carries with it certain limitations on the timber types that may be available for purchase. The regional potentialities are described in the book *Regional Silviculture,*[2] referred to in Chapter III. Within any region, however, two types of timber stands may be found. The ecologist designates these as pioneer types and climax types. The pioneer types are those that reclaim abandoned fields or heavily burned areas, or areas that otherwise have been severely treated in the past. Usually, these types are made up of trees having small windblown seeds that carry for long distances. Aspen and cottonwood are outstanding examples. Others include the birches, alder, pines, ash, maple, elm, yellow poplar, and in northern areas, spruce. The climax types are those that develop over a long period of time and tend to hold the land against invasion by other species. In the northern United States it is the northern hardwoods and in upper elevations, spruce-fir; in the northwestern United States, western red cedar, true firs, and hemlock; in the southern United States, various hardwoods. Oftentimes the pioneer type is more valuable for timber production and more esthetically desirable than is the climax type. The pines of the southern coastal plain tend to be more valuable than the hardwoods that succeed them. In the northern United States, white pine and the pioneer hardwood species, yellow birch, black cherry, and white ash are of high value and more important for timber than hemlock and beech that may succeed them.

It should be kept in mind, however, that all trees have what is recognized as a botanical range, and a much narrower commercial range. For example, though black cherry has a wide range, it attains its largest size and best quality in the western Allegheny Plateau and northern Appalachians. In northern New England it is a marginal tree. Soils, too, influence the growth of trees. Yellow poplar and white ash may occur on thin, rocky soils but are unlikely to produce high-quality timber on such lands. For these reasons, it is well to have advice from a local forester concerning which species and types do well in the locality.

A forest property having a large percentage of high-value trees is, of course, a better investment than one with low-value species. Where market conditions are favorable for trees of pulpwood size, in the Lake States, for example, a pioneer forest cover of aspen or jack pine that already has a mixture of longer-lived and more valuable species offers a good income opportunity, because the short-lived species can be harvested at an early age and the longer lived ones held for sawtimber.

The forest owner can maintain his land in pioneer types by heavy cutting and proper soil preparation. To convert a pioneer type to a climax type in less than one tree generation, on the other hand, is difficult. Much can be done, however, by maintaining the proper density and favoring the right trees.

Many pioneer stands are less than ideal. They may contain a large number of trees that become established early and over-top the others. These are usually limby and of little value for timber use. Where market conditions are such that coarse-limbed trees can be harvested, they should be taken off the land as early as possible to favor the quality trees that are standing beneath them. Open-grown oaks, cherry, elm, sugar maple, and white pine are often of limited or no value to the sawmill or veneer operator. In some circumstances, it may even be desirable to deaden them if they have no market value.

Timber Volumes

The value of the trees standing on a forest property depends upon their species, quality, and volume. Timber volumes are determined by a timber inventory, or cruise. This inventory should be made by a properly qualified forester who has had local experience and is in a position to estimate the quality of the timber as well as its volume. A timber inventory estimate may be based on a 100 per cent cruise, where every tree is measured and tallied, or upon a sampling of an area and conversion of the volume on the sampled area for the total area involved. The accuracy of a sample cruise will depend upon the number of measured plots in the sample, their relationship to the total area, and the variability of the timber stand. An experienced forester can furnish an estimate of the accuracy of his cruise data.

Where large areas are involved, timber estimates are made by combining an analysis of aerial photographs with data measured on field plots. For timber tracts of two hundred acres or less, dependence is usually on a ground cruise alone, with an aerial photo being used for verification of areas of timber types.

In an analysis of the value of standing timber, it should be recognized that a forest tract having an average timber volume of less than 1,500 board feet per acre can seldom be logged economically. Such properties, if well stocked with young trees that will soon grow into merchantability, often may be the most favorable purchases for the forest owner. He must, however, count on waiting ten years or more before he can expect to harvest anything from such lands. Forested tracts having 5,000 or more board feet per acre in the East are, generally, avidly sought by timber operators and, hence, difficult to find. The forest owner must compete with the logger to acquire such properties. It is just such properties, however, that offer the best opportunity for early forest operations and that can be expected to meet carrying charges for holding them. The field examination of the forest property, therefore, should take this into consideration, in addition to topography, soil, markets, timber species, timber quality, timber volumes, and the prospect of timber growth during the next decade.

The forest property seeker should try to acquire properties capable of providing merchantable timber within a ten-year period and from which enough timber may be cut to cover a part of the carrying costs. Where such partial harvests are contemplated, care should be taken to be sure that the property still has a good productive residual stand left for future growth after cutting. The help of an experienced forester is needed to make such a determination. By study and practice the forest owner, himself, may acquire sufficient experience to appraise a property containing standing timber. Details are available from the series of forest textbooks and handbooks suggested for study in the Appendix.

Appraisal of the Property

The appraisal of a forest property may be made by the prospective purchaser or his agent after an examination of the topography, soil, timber types, volume and growth rate, markets, and accessibility. This appraisal will give the owner an idea of the property's current liquidation value. One should keep in mind, however, that such an appraisal differs from that made by a professional land appraiser. His determinations are based on what the going land exchange prices are in the area under consideration. The typical land appraisal, though highly useful in bargaining with the prospective seller, gives little or no information to the buyer on what its value may be to him as a timber-producing property. For this kind of appraisal the reader will wish to consider the information set forth in Chapter II as it applies to the specific property under consideration. The spread in income potential between good properties and poor ones is so large that careful on-the-ground evaluation is necessary. To carry out this sort of evaluation, the prospective buyer will find no substitute for a competent local forester. The following is not an unusual experience. After showing a prospective buyer over his two hundred acre uncut woodland, Bill Sawyer, a sawmill owner, remarked:

"Mr. Forester, I have an offer of twenty dollars an acre for this land. What do you think it is worth to your client?"

Forester: "I think you should accept the offer you have."

Mr. Sawyer, somewhat dismayed: "There's a great deal of timber on the lot, and trees grow fast."

Forester: "Then you had better keep it for yourself. It's worth more to you than to my client because you're in the lumber business."

Mr. Sawyer: "Well, how much is it worth to your client?"

Forester: "Nothing. Your two hundred acres lie on a dry, south-facing slope. Growth is very slow, except along the drainage channel. He couldn't afford to own this land because the value of the timber growth wouldn't equal the annual taxes, not to mention other unavoidable costs."

The buyer is best prepared if he has an evaluation made both by a land appraiser and a forester. The former will give him the best estimate of going market prices, hence of the possibilities of getting his money back if he would be forced to sell within the next few years. The forester's evaluation will cover the current timber value with an estimate of the increase during the next ten years.

Predicting future timber growth is an involved process requiring the aid of a trained forester. For many regions general guides are available to interested landowners. Such a guide for New York State is available in the bulletin *Timber Growth Rates for Natural Forest Stands in New York State.*[3] Information is also available in the *Forestry Handbook,*[4] by Forbes and Meyer.

The buyer also needs additional information on estimated carrying charges and possible returns during the ten-year period.

The nature of costs was outlined in Chapter II. He now needs to know what such costs are likely to be on the property he is considering buying. Interest and custodial costs he may know, and current taxes can be ascertained from the town or county clerk's office. If the buyer is to pay for a title search and survey, he should consult a title examiner and surveyor. For a timber estimate and general estimate of carrying charges, the consulting forester's advice should be sought, as well as for the costs of a timber sale and other forest improvements. Most consulting foresters can, in fact, readily obtain all such information for a client.

The value for timber production must often be based on the potential value some ten years hence, discounted to the present, with appropriate allowances made for interest, carrying charges, and risk. It is with such information at hand that the purchaser is in a position to approach a landowner with an offer on the property.

Purchase Negotiation

Land purchase can usually be carried out best if the owner has let it be known that the land is for sale and has mentioned his price. A preliminary examination can then be made with the owner to locate the boundaries and get a general idea of the property. If experienced, one may do this himself; if not, it is advisable to employ a consultant forester to act as land agent in carrying out this task and others involved in land purchasing, If the preliminary examination reveals that the property is one the prospective purchaser wishes to acquire, and if the price is known to be within an acceptable range, a detailed timber cruise and other expensive examination on the ground may be omitted. If the land has recently been cut over, as will often be the case, an estimate of the remaining timber volume and values can usually be made from a cursory examination. If high timber values and a consequently higher asking price are involved, then the buyer should negotiate an option with the owner and proceed to make a detailed timber estimate and appraisal. A contract or agreement to purchase may then be entered into, assuming that the detailed examination reveals the values present to equal or exceed the offering price. A purchase contract should specify a legal description of the property, the area, the purchase price agreed upon, the time which is available to the purchaser for examination, the date for closing the sale, the type of deed to be furnished, and the title examination.

Legal Considerations

The purchase of land involves an investment that the owner wants to protect. Therefore, he should never enter into any hasty land transactions. In order to protect himself from excessive prices, future land restrictions, faulty deeds, and numerous other problems, a lawyer should be consulted before an agreement is made concerning the purchase of land. Lawyers can be most helpful in drawing contracts for land transfer because they can anticipate most of the technical problems and can word the contract accordingly. It is also advisable to discuss one's objectives with an attorney so that he can act in one's best interests. A well recommended local lawyer has the double advantage of knowing both the law and the local people with whom the new owner will be dealing.

The considerable information that he may have on local properties for sale may also save a purchaser time and money.

The future landowner should be aware of the legal aspects of land transfer and the restrictions of land ownership. By having such an awareness, he will be more appreciative of the services a lawyer can provide.

Contracts

The law of contracts is an invaluable aid to land transfer, provided the parties involved understand the basic principles of contract law and know how they affect the buyer and the seller. All contracts, whether written or oral, must include the following essential elements before the contract can be enforced by a court of law. If any of these elements is not present, the contract can be declared void.

Contract essentials: [5]

1) *Competent persons.* Persons who cannot make enforceable contracts are aliens, insane persons, drunkards, minors, and corporations having charters that prohibit their making contracts.

2) *Mutual agreement.* Both persons must voluntarily agree to the offer and the acceptance of the contract and act in good faith.

3) *Legal subject matter.* The act to be performed, or the thing to be done, must not violate any laws or statutes, nor can it be contrary to public policy.

4) *Consideration.* This is the price or other valuable considerations to be exchanged.

5) *Proper form.* The contract to sell land must be written, stating the price, the time limits, and the terms of payment.

Conveyances of Land

Deeds are the most common form of transferring "real property," or "land." A deed is a contract of sale transferring the ownership of land from the seller to the buyer, and a land deed includes all standing timber, buildings, and all other things attached to the land unless specifically excluded in the deed. Conveyance of land by deed does not transfer the rights to the previous owner's personal property. It generally terminates all minor rights, such as those by licensees. Personal property includes all items that can be moved from place to place. Personal property can become real property if it is fixed to the land. For example, a pile of lumber is personal property. If used to build a garage, it becomes real property. The reverse is also true. Standing trees are considered real property in most states until they are cut. Once a tree is cut down, it becomes personal property.

Land Survey

Another basic consideration is the legal boundaries of the land to be purchased. The deed must describe clearly, beyond any doubt, the property's boundaries. The buyer of land should be able to locate the exterior boundaries of his property by the legal description given in the deed. If he cannot, he should obtain the services of a registered land surveyor. Properties were surveyed by the metes and bounds system in the thirteen original states, and because of the crudeness of these early surveys, the services of a licensed surveyor who has had experience in relocating old boundary lines should be sought. Consulting foresters often do land acquisition and surveying work as one of their specialties. A consulting forester who performs this type of work may be more adept at re-establishing original corners and boundaries, owing to his training and familiarity with the numerous tree species and their remains in stumps.

The surveyor or prospective landowner should get in touch with the owners of adjoining lands to go over the boundaries. Agreement between these owners is usually sufficient to establish the boundaries. Old fence lines are often good evidence of a boundary. A woven wire fence originally attached to posts will usually be found to run straight and to follow the line described in the deed. If the owner points out such a fence as the boundary and the neighbor agrees to it, this may be accepted. Prompt measures should be taken to mark such a boundary in the forest before all posts decay and disappear. It is surprising how rapidly signs of such a fence are obliterated by fallen leaves and vegetation once the posts tip over.

Barbed wire stapled to trees may indicate the general vicinity of the boundary. Such a fence tends to weave in and out to reach trees on which to attach the wire. It may be off the line by twenty or more feet and is likely to be slightly within the property of the original fence builder. If corners can be located, a new line should be established by survey. A well-run compass line may suffice if both owners agree to it. Generally a survey will also bring to light any use of the property by other than the owner. If a neighbor or anyone else has been using the property for grazing livestock or for access to his own land, or has maintained a structure on the land, he may be able to establish a right to such use if his use has been of sufficient duration. If the old deed description was imprecise, the new survey should be incorporated in the new deed, together with other descriptive material on the property boundaries and previous ownership. Surveys are described in property deeds which are recorded in the county courthouse. Owing to the nature of the written description found on deeds, the property deed should be checked against the description in the courthouse to ensure that no mistakes have been made in copying the boundary description. In a boundary location dispute the decision rendered by the court, based on the results of the surveyor's findings, is the deciding factor.

Deeds

There are three basic types of deeds: the quit-claim deed, the grant deed or limited warranty deed, and the warranty deed. The quit-claim deed merely conveys to the buyer whatever interest the seller has in the property. The person offering the quit-claim deed as a title of ownership may not be the actual full owner of the property but, instead, a person who has some minor interest in the property. A quit-claim deed never guarantees, but simply releases, the seller's interest. "This type of deed is often used where ownership title is unclear and the buyer wishes to protect himself by acquiring all possible interests."[6]

The grant deed is the one that is most common in land conveyance. It is considered a limited warranty deed in that it has the implied warranty that the seller has done nothing to void his own title. The limitation of this deed is that it gives the buyer no protection against title defects acquired when the seller bought the land, but this limitation can be covered in large measure by careful title examination or by title insurance.

Under the provisions of a warranty deed, the seller guarantees the title and is required by law to protect the buyer against all known and unknown defects. In other words, the seller promises the buyer that he will not be troubled with any claims or encumbrances on the land. If the seller's title should ever be proved fraudulent or faulty, the buyer has a legal claim against the seller. Since the seller may die, move away, or become financially insolvent, the prudent purchaser will want to take further steps to assure himself of a good title. Up-to-date tax and title searches should be supplied, preferably by the seller. The title search which should go back fifty years or more, should be examined by a title attorney before the purchase is consummated. Further protection can be had through title insurance, but this kind of insurance may be expensive for forest land. The owner may prefer to accept this risk, spreading it over his several acquisitions as a form of self-insurance.

Tax Deeds

Occasionally it may be possible to acquire forest land at

county tax sales. A tax deed is furnished by the county treasurer upon such a purchase. Theoretically, a county tax deed wipes out all previous claims to the land, but in reality it may not do so at all. Legal opinion differs rather widely on the soundness of a tax deed. Such a deed does, however, give the buyer the protection that any claimant must refund with interest the money the buyer has invested in the land if the claim is to be redeemed.

A seller who holds only a tax deed to his land will usually agree to furnish only a quit-claim deed. The burden of title clearance then rests with the purchaser. The value of the tax deed increases with the length of time the seller has owned it and the extent to which he has occupied or used the land. The estate purchaser will probably be obliged to acquire some lands that have defective titles. This involves a risk, but often one that it is best to assume rather than not to acquire a strategic parcel of land. Prompt measures to assert the rights of ownership will help to establish the right to the land. Also, legal means exist for clearing the title. Since length of ownership and use are factors in establishing rights to the land, legal steps may be postponed unless the property is a particularly valuable one to the purchaser. It behooves the new owner, however, not to make valuable investments such as buildings, roads, or artificial lakes on property he acquired by tax deed.

The statute of limitations states the period of time within which legal action can be instituted, based on the nature of the action. It merely forces a person with a claim to present the claim to a court of law before the time period elapses. Failure to bring action within the time period gives the defendant a defense. The following statute of limitations applies to New York State only:

1) Injury to property   3 years
2) Most written contracts   6 years
3) Recovery of real property   15 years
4) Judgments   20 years

The above discussion concerns the transfer of land by purchase. Land can also be acquired by gift or inheritance, exchange, or recovery from a government agency.

Restrictions of Land Ownership

No landowner is an absolute monarch over his property. There are restrictions contained in land titles and others imposed by law to which the landowner must adhere:

> In its purest sense, ownership means complete dominion, title, or proprietary right in a thing or claim. As we know it, however, ownership is a rather loose aggregation of human relationships that provides maximum, though limited, use and possession of property objects.[7]

Society has the following powers to regulate private land use: power of escheat, eminent domain, police power, taxation and assessments, and permits and licenses.

The power of escheat is based upon the concept that all land has an owner, since no rights can exist without an owner. If a private owner is deceased and there are no relatives to inherit his land, the land passes by escheat to a unit of government.

The right to eminent domain is the right of a governmental body to take real property for public use. This right is exercised when land is needed for such things as highways or school sites. A fair price or just compensation, as determined by an impartial arbiter, must be paid the private owner by the governmental body exercising the right.

Police power is broad in scope and involves the enactment of statutes, regulations, and ordinances by the government to regulate the use of real property for the welfare of the public. The enactment of zoning laws is an exercise of the most common type of police power. Through zoning restrictions government regulates land use, construction of buildings, and the type of buildings. Other police power rights involve landlord-tenant relations, property liens, and procedure for recording deeds and titles.

The most familiar right exercised by the government is taxation of property. The tax on land and buildings is based on an assessment made by the local tax assessor. If the tax is not paid within a given period of time, the land may be sold by the governmental unit to recover the unpaid taxes. By adjusting the assessment rates, the governmental unit can also regulate the use of land. Landowners may have any one of, or all of, the following real property tax bills which may come at different times during the year: state, town, county, and school.

Public agencies use permits and licenses extensively to impose conditions on resource use. Hunting and fishing licenses are two illustrative examples. Permits are also used extensively in the field of water supply and development in most states.

Water Law and Property Rights[8]

A water right is usually treated as real property in that it is a right to use the water flowing in a natural water course, but it is not a right to corpus. Since water rights are treated as real property, they may be obtained through condemnation under the power of eminent domain.

The water right doctrine in the eastern United States is based upon the premise that the owner of the land bordering a stream has the right to use the water on his land. This relationship of land to the water is known as the riparian doctrine. If land does not touch the body of water, the landowner has no right to its use. A landowner may not divert or alter the natural flow of the water, nor may he use the water unreasonably. The application of the riparian doctrine, which is based on common law, is complex, has many limitations, and is often contradictory. Before a landowner with riparian rights can be sure of his exact rights under his specific circumstances, he should consult a lawyer. If the lawyer is uncertain, a verdict by a jury in a court of law is necessary to establish these rights.

Ground water rights, also based on common law, have few

if any restrictions. The strict right of a landowner permits him to pump off-the-ground water, even though he may be draining a neighbor's ground water. A court may prevent a landowner from unlimited use of ground water if he injures his neighbor's water supply willfully. In New York State a permit is required to operate or install wells that pump more than 100,000 gallons daily in most Long Island counties.

Other important limitations are easements, claims, liens, excavations, nuisances, and subsurface rights. These are not all the limitations but only the more common ones. If there are any restrictions written in the deed, the prospective purchaser should discuss them with his lawyer to find out what they involve and how they will affect the owner's objectives.

Easements. An easement is a permanent right, usually acquired by deed, to use real property that belongs to another. A permanent easement can be acquired by usage, by traveling across a property for a number of years as fixed by law on a given route.

> Easements such as grazing rights or the use of a road may be prevented by charging fees, or by blocking the road for a short period of time once a year and advertising the blockage in the local paper. An actual right is given by law to a landowner to reach his property. This is an easement by necessity.[9]

In order to avoid legal disputes, if one purchases a property that is landlocked (must cross private property to reach his own property), he should make sure the "right of ingress, egress, and regress" is stated clearly in his deed.

Claims. A claim is an assertion of title, which must be settled by a court of law

Liens. Unpaid taxes, improvements, mortgages, and assessments for which no payment has been made are the basis for a lien on a property. If the land is sold, the lien is enforceable against the new owner.

Nuisances. A property owner cannot cause nuisances such as eyesores or excessive noise and smoke that affect the owners of adjacent lands.

Excavations. An excavation cannot be dug so close to the

property boundary that the neighbor's land on the other side of the boundary will cave in.

Surface, subsurface, and supersurface rights in land. [10] Ownership of the surface is separate from the ownership of the strata. Both owners of surface and subsurface have certain joint rights to the land surface, such as trespass at all times. Conflicts often arise when the owners attempt to exercise their rights. Separation of surface and subsurface rights is a recent development in the United States law system. As a result, legal precedents are not well established. Separate sub-surface ownership usually occurs only where mineral or oil resources are anticipated.

Asserting Ownership

As soon as the new owner has acquired his deed, checked it for accuracy, and had it examined by his attorney, he should record it with the county clerk or recorder of deeds. It is wise also to notify the tax collector of his purchase so that tax notices will be sent to him rather than to the former owner. In this manner he informs officials that he is, in fact, the new owner of the property.

Since title to land in some cases may be dependent upon occupancy and use, the new owner should promptly assert his ownership. Thus he should notify tenants or other occupants of his ownership and arrange to collect rent, have them sign a new lease, or have them vacate the premises. He should also establish the corners and blaze or paint various points along the boundary lines. These markings will serve notice to owners of adjoining lands concerning what the purchaser considers the proper boundaries to be. If any dispute arises, it can be settled promptly. Well-marked boundaries and corners are a great help in managing the property and in making timber sales. Marking boundaries and establishing corners should be done promptly following the property survey while the lines can easily be followed.

If the owner wishes to reserve hunting rights to himself,

the land should be legally posted by putting up signs around the boundaries with his name printed somewhere on the poster. He should, however, weigh the value to him of "no trespassing" signs against the ill-will they may create among those accustomed to hunting on his land.

Other acts of ownership include tree planting, thinning, or other forest stand improvement operations, road construction, erection of a summer home or camp, sale of forest products, and leasing of various user rights. The employment of a local custodian to watch the property for the owner not only guards against unauthorized use but also tends to confirm ownership. Visiting the property frequently and establishing friendly relations with neighbors further confirms one's use and, hence, accepted ownership of the property.

SUMMARY

The purchase of a forest property involves the following steps:

1) Locating the property and owner and making a preliminary examination on the ground.

2) Negotiating or buying an option or a contract of sale that specifies price, title clearance, time for detailed examination, date of closure, and other pertinent details, pending actual purchase of the property.

3) Making a detailed examination to arrive at a determination of boundaries and area by survey; an estimate of timber types, volume, and values; an estimate of productivity for timber growing and other anticipated use; and an appraisal of the value of the property to the buyer. Should the appraised value be less than the price, either the purchase must be given up, together with the option fee, or a new price negotiated with the owner.

4) Examining and verifying the title to be conveyed.

5) Making payment and signing the deed.

6) Recording the deed in the county clerk's office.

Once these steps have all been taken, the new owner should set about to assert his ownership of the land by acts of use on the ground.

The area of land transfer and limitations of rights is rather complicated. This detailed discussion has been included to put the prospective forest purchaser on guard against some of the problems and difficulties he may face. It is all too easy to acquire a quit-claim deed to a piece of property from an alleged owner only to find later that the land had been sold at a tax sale some two or more years earlier, that there are outstanding judgments against a previous owner, that an heir's interest has not been acquired in the transaction, or that assessments against the property are outstanding. Only by having a competent title search and tax search made and having these examined by a lawyer can the owner have confidence in his deed. Although such precautions may seem costly, they are necessary assurances against possible problems and expenses of major consequence in the future.

LITERATURE CITED

1. John Preston, *Developing Farm Woodlands* (New York: McGraw-Hill, 1954), 160.

2. John W. Barrett, ed., *Regional Silviculture of the United States* (New York: Ronald Press, 1962), 610.

3. Miles J. Ferree and Robert K. Hagar, *Timber Growth Rates for Natural Forest Stands in New York State,* State University of New York College of Forestry *Technical Publication 78* (Syracuse, N.Y., 1956), 56.

4. Reginald D. Forbes and Arthur B. Meyer, *Forestry Handbook* (New York: Ronald Press, 1955), Sec. 1, pp. 90-98.

5. Robert R. Rosenberg, *College Business Law* (New York: McGraw-Hill, 1953), 5.

6. Harry W. Falk, *Timber and Forest Products Law* (Berkeley, Calif.: Howell-North, 1958), 19.

7. *Land (The Yearbook of Agriculture)* (Washington, D.C.: U.S. Government Printing Office, 1958), 289.

8. Jack Hirshleifer, James C. DeHaven, and Jerry Milliman, *Water Supply* (Chicago: University of Chicago Press, 1960), 232-33.

9. H. A. Meyer, A. B. Recknagel, and D. D. Stevenson, *Forest Management* (New York: Ronald Press, 1951), 29.

10. Roland R. Renne, *Land Economics* (New York: Harper & Bros., 1947),122.

 V

Managing the Forest Property

The Role of the Owner

Throughout this book repeated attention has been called to the need for seeking professional assistance on specific tasks. Need also exists to use such help in the broader task of preparing a management plan for the property. But however large the consultant's role may be, having a consultant in no way absolves the owner from responsibility for ultimate decisions. It is he who must decide whether or not to embark on forest landownership, who decides on location, size of holding, and objectives of ownership. It is he who provides the funds for acquisition and operation and who must adjust his ambitions to his purse. It is he and his wife and children who will use the estate, and only they can decide on how much they can afford to pay for the satisfactions it yields them. The owner must decide on whether to build a pond, plant an open field, build a road, thin a young stand, make a timber sale, or operate a Christmas tree plantation, and who must make the many other decisions necessary for responsible property management. Such decisions form the base for management planning.

Forest management has been defined as "the application of business methods and technical forestry principles to the operation of a forest property." To the private forest owner a definition of management may need to be broader than this, for he is concerned not only with the business of forestry but with esthetic values and personal satisfactions. We may say, therefore, that forest management covers all of those activities carried out to achieve the objectives of the owner. These may be simple or complex and varied, but one point is clear: no man is likely to assume the considerable expense and exert the effort required to assemble a forest estate unless he has a strong urge to do so and has definite objectives in mind.

Management Produces both Public and Private Benefits

Ownership of a sizable forest property carries with it implied obligations to manage it with the public, as well as private, interest in mind. The products and services of forests are too broad and important to be managed in such a way that few benefits from the land accrue to society in general. Most owners will gain considerable satisfaction in developing the property so that it becomes a good long-term, income-producing investment. Fortunately, the public interest and the private interest coincide at this point because selling timber and other forest products and services, as well as paying taxes, are the primary means by which the public interest is served through responsible management of the property.

It may be argued that the public benefits whether the timber is cut or not; in fact, some believe that the benefits to society are greater when the forest is not used for its timber value, even though good forestry methods are followed in harvesting merchantable trees. This is a mistaken opinion that stems from the unsightliness of a forest recently cut over on an imprudent and irresponsible "logger's choice" basis. But logger's choice and good forestry methods are usually wide apart.

Cutting, properly done, transfers the growth potential of the forest from trees of low timber value to those of high value, hastening the growth of the latter. Carefully cut forests provide more timber than do unmanaged forests because trees are harvested from the managed forest that otherwise would die; better timber is produced because only the best trees are allowed to survive.

Here is one of the rewards of applied forestry. This very high-quality white pine developed following the removal of crooked, coarse-limbed trees from the stand thirty years earlier. It contrasts sharply with its unmanaged counter-part of wide-spreading, heavy-branched trees that produce but grade 3, 4, and 5 common lumber.

Forests Are Conditioned to Change

Some people may protest that harvesting timber upsets the balance of nature. But man must use nature's productive potential if he is to live on this earth at all. Man, together with all other kinds of living creatures, is incessantly engaged in upsetting the balance of nature, whether to his good or hurt. It is the nature of life to do so. Maintaining civilized society demands changes in nature's balance, and there is no more reason not to harvest mature timber than not to harvest mature wheat, cotton, or hay.

The virgin forest of North America endured for centuries with relatively minor interference by civilization but not without disturbance. The Indians were known to set fire to forests and prairies as a means of making their hunting easier. They used fire to clear patches for cultivation, and they were also quick to take advantage of burned areas in their search for berries and for the wildlife which these areas attracted. Moreover, the usual concept is that the virgin forest undergoes little change, but a static forest is seldom encountered in nature. Extensive studies of forests, even of forests of the northern hardwood type, which is considered to be an ideal example of a climax forest—one that has reached a stable state—refute this concept. Instead of being made up of trees of all ages, the virgin forest is found to contain but a few age classes. These classes become established following windthrow, fire, heavy insect outbreaks, or other catastrophes. The old trees tend to reach maturity at approximately the same time. When something occurs that weakens one tree, it may also weaken many others. A tree in its decline removes support from others that may cause trees to die in groups or even over wide areas. The virgin forest is not static but highly dynamic, with substantial changes occurring continuously to maintain the natural health and succession of trees and of wildlife.

Consequently, when any forest contains a predominance of old, mature and overmature trees, nature is not in balance but out of balance. Natural catastrophes rejuvenate the forest by removing the old trees over a wide area, making room for younger successors. Individual tree species killed by insects or fungi also make room for new trees. The hand of the skillful forester is far more gentle in maintaining a vigorous forest than is the undiscriminating hand of nature.

There are other reasons for man to manage the forest, aside from the necessity of obtaining timber for commerce. Water supplies are needed, for one thing, as well as wildlife, recreation areas, and forage for livestock. Here again, the popular conception of the role of forests is a greatly oversimplified and often erroneous one.

Judicious Cutting Augments Water Yields

More and more, the amount and quality of water supplies are becoming critically important. The forest provides excellent protection for regular yields of usable water, but considerably less than maximum water yields prevail where no timber cutting has occurred. Large quantities of water are lost through evaporation and used by the trees themselves. A dense canopy intercepts a considerable amount of rainfall— more than one-half of the total fall of a light shower. Although some water eventually does drip through or run down the tree trunks, up to one-tenth inch of the average rainstorm may be intercepted and lost quickly by evaporation. A cumulative loss of 8 to 15 per cent of the annual precipitation may occur owing to interception by, and evaporation from, the crowns of trees in northern hardwood stands. Interception of snow by conifers in winter may be even more significant, as research studies at Fraser, Colorado, have shown. Large trees draw heavily upon soil water for their own use, especially during the growing season. Most of this water is lost into the atmosphere through transpiration. Experiments at the government's Coweeta Hydrologic Laboratory at Franklin, North Carolina, show that a hardwood forest cover during the growing season may remove as much as seventeen inches of water over a watershed, or more than one-fifth of total rainfall. Partial cutting reduced the total water use by the forest approximately in proportion to the volume of timber cut. When one realizes how expensive are modern water impoundments for municipal use, he can readily understand that an excess of large trees, especially along water courses, is a real luxury.

Timber Management Favors Wildlife

Food and cover for wildlife is in greater supply in areas where constructive timber management has been practiced. Wild turkey, deer, rabbits, and many other mammals are dependent upon forest foods, but an overdense forest cover eliminates most low-growing food plants. In the uncut forest, food areas exist only in places where old trees have died or have been blown over to create openings in the forest canopy. Also, more seed are produced by trees with free crowns than those crowded in an uncut stand. Ground feeders include also those birds and mammals that feed on insects, earthworms, and other soil animals. A dense conifer covering, especially of spruce, not only prevents the growth of herbs and shrubs but maintains acid soil unfavorable to earthworms and other soil fauna. These soil dwellers break down the litter to release plant nutrients, manufacture humus, maintain soil tilth, and open channels for penetration of roots and water. Thus, they improve the watershed for municipal and industrial supplies. A managed forest, because it has trees of different sizes and ages and because it has a less dense canopy than natural stands, offers a greater and more varied fare for soil organisms and wildlife and better protective cover than the unmanaged forest. Where conscious efforts are made to improve wildlife habitat through forest management, the carrying capacity can be greatly increased.

Bird lovers are aware that some species, notably certain warblers, vacate a forest after clear-cutting. But even the most shy return within two to three years after the new forest growth reaches head height, plus additional species not previously seen in the uncut forest.

Judicious cuttings that create improved wildlife food and cover also improve forage for domestic livestock. The forage for livestock beneath a heavy forest canopy is very limited.

The Well-Managed Forest Is Inviting to the Recreationist

Some people contend that a forest in which no trees are cut is more pleasant to be in than is the managed forest. This is mostly a matter of viewpoint. A true wilderness is just that, and most men avoid it; otherwise it would not exist. Esthetically, the untended forest has a shabby, untidy appearance with broken-topped, lodged and fallen trees, dead or spike-topped trees, and badly formed trees. Moreover, its susceptibility to periodic catastrophes such as windthrow, disease, and insect outbreaks can create both unsightliness and a heavy fire risk, and cause hazardous and almost impenetrable conditions. Moreover, the absence of logging roads makes it difficult to walk and easy to get lost. Without access, protection against fire becomes very costly and difficult. So, even for recreational use, the unmanaged forest has many drawbacks.

One other point needs to be made: the undeveloped woodland area that an owner may today acquire in the settled region of the United States is not an undisturbed forest; rather, it is one from which many trees have been cut, repeatedly, over several generations of man's use. Often the larger trees that remain are those that were considered unmarketable by the owner or the logger in earlier operations. Usually the species composition of the forest has also been widely modified. Pines may have given way to hardwoods, or the valuable hardwoods have become dominated by beech, elm, hop-hornbeam, hickory, and other undesired species. Allowing such defective trees or low-value species to occupy the soil indefinitely at the expense of ash, cherry, maple, tulip poplar, and others far more desirable and more capable of building up a favorable environment is certainly not good for the forest. Also, it produces no valuable lumber or other products to support our economy.

The authors admit to displaying the forester's bias in urging that private forests be managed. Those who love the wilderness seek other values—solitude, naturalness, remoteness, and freedom from the trappings of modern life. These can be achieved only to a limited extent on a private forest estate, though a forest property can and should provide the owner a considerable degree of seclusion and freedom from human disturbance as well as opportunity to appreciate and enjoy a close communion with nature.

The best evidence of the recreational use of managed forests is to be found in Europe where hikers, cyclists, bird watchers, picnickers, and mountain climbers throng the commercially managed forests on weekends and holidays. Roads and trails built for wood extraction serve the recreationist as they do the landowner, in total utility.

Management Planning

The desires of the owner of a forest holding are so personal, the property he acquires so unique, and the complexity of fitting his desires to his property so great that developing a plan of operation becomes an important and individual task. The task is one that should be promptly undertaken because the management plan will guide his decisions over a reasonable period into the future, usually a decade. In all probability, he will seek early assistance from his consultant forester in such planning.

The management plan is a carefully reasoned document that states the owner's objectives, assigns priorities to them, lists the resources of the property, weighs these in terms of the objectives, and sets forth a plan of operation to achieve definite goals over the planning period. This plan should cover any additional land acquisitions and the anticipated expenditures for this purpose. It should list the various resources of the land and indicate the potential for producing income and other satisfactions.

The plan should outline a schedule of operations including such operations as tree planting, pruning, and thinning, sale of timber or Christmas trees, and the construction of roads and other major structures such as camps and garages. It should consider the total timber volumes and timber growth and include a timber cutting schedule for the period. A statement of rotation age or desired tree size and type of timber stand management to be followed should be part of the plan, and cutting cycles that are practicable and within the capacity of the forest should be projected; along with this, the standards of commercial buyers should be considered. A statement of investments in subsidiary enterprises such as commercial recreation developments and land leasing and the sale of minor forest products should be outlined, and a time schedule for each operation should be included. From all these, the owner can set up a tentative budget of income and expenditures by years. His projected budget should also indicate the amount of public aid he expects to receive to help with his forest improvement projects.

What the management plan does, in effect, is to place before the owner his plan of operation for the next decade along with the anticipated outlays and revenues. If his plans are relatively simple, the management plan is simple. If they are more complicated, the plan will necessarily be longer and more involved. The plan should be flexible enough to allow minor adjustments as circumstances dictate, but it should not be ignored or else there is no reason for preparing it. The advantage of the management plan is that it enables the owner to make his day-to-day and year-to-year decisions in line with a ten-year outline and, hence, guard against hasty and unwarranted optimism, pessimism, or opportunism in these decisions.

There are other reasons for preparing a careful management

plan. Should the owner die or become incapacitated, his estate administrator and heirs would have available a carefully prepared document outlining what expenditures of effort and money are anticipated and giving some idea of the revenues that might be expected from the property. Thereby they will be in a position to decide whether to retain it as an income-producing investment or sell it. The existence of a carefully prepared written management plan is also concrete evidence of the owner's intent and, hence, excellent evidence to refute the contention of a tax examiner that the property is used solely for personal recreation.

Reassessment of Objectives

The first step in management planning is to reassess objectives. Once the property has been acquired, forest ownership it is no longer a dream but reality. Objectives that were clearly formed in the beginning need to be re-examined in terms of the capacity of the property to meet them. A unique situation now exists because the owner with his objectives now has a specific piece of property on which he must work. The plan for property management cannot be lifted from a textbook or borrowed from the state forester. It must be prepared by the owner himself with the help of his forest consultant.

In the reassessment of objectives the new forest property owner should ask himself such questions as the following:

1) How many of my original objectives can be met on the property I have?

2) Do these objectives need to be rearranged in priority?

3) Have I reserved enough funds to acquire additional property to meet objectives that cannot be realized on what I now own?

4) To what should I give first attention in order to fulfill the purposes for which I bought the property?

5) How can I best begin to reap some of the advantages and satisfactions of forest ownership?

6) In view of experience to date, what is the total investment that I can afford to make in a forest property?

7) If additional land is needed for my purposes, how much and what type of land should I seek to acquire?

8) What are the prospects of immediate income from a timber sale on the property so that some capital may be recaptured for additional investment in land or development? And, would such a sale be wise?

9) What subsidiary sources of income other than sale of timber are possible? Am I in a position to lease hunting and fishing rights, to lease summer homesites or actually sell them, to embark on Christmas tree growing, or to run a commercial campground for summer visitors?

10) What investment should be made soon in timber stand improvement, planting, thinning, and other cultural measures?

11) What is the long-term prospect of income and how may this be distributed in time?

12) How much time can I spend on the property?

Other questions also are likely to arise requiring prompt decision before the owner may embark on additional purchases to round out the property. It is well to list all objectives, classifying them into those strictly of a business nature and those that are obviously for personal or family pleasure. Some of the objectives may be dual in nature; that is, afford some recreation or training for children and also some opportunity for income. The construction of a pond for family use is obviously for personal pleasure. But if one digs a pond or lake and erects cabins around it for rental to the public, the entire investment may be allowable as a business expense.

Outline for Management Plan

No general outline will serve for all forest properties. The outline given below is a moderately complex one. For more detail, the reader is referred to books cited in the Bibliography.

I. *The objectives of the owner.* These have been repeatedly emphasized. It is important that the business and personal use objectives be separately listed and provided for in the plan. Priorities should be indicated.

II. *Description.* A general description of the locality, covering roads and other transportation systems, general economy of the region, local industry, status of agriculture, the soil conditions, topography and forest types, availability of forest labor, timber operators and locations, distances to various market outlets for forest products, and a general picture of other outside factors such as taxes and public protection from theft and fire that may influence the opportunities for acquiring or selling land and carrying out the plan should be prepared. This section, though it need not be elaborate, will help both the owner and his successor to realize the opportunities that are available locally for successful forest management. This is simply setting down in a concise way for ready reference the material outlined in Chapters I and III.

III. *Forest data.* A description of the forest property giving location, boundaries, maps, division into working compartments, and a summary of timber volumes and growth constitutes this part.

IV. *Protection of the forest.* This portion should outline the extent of protection provided by the state against fire and insect and disease outbreaks and list any supplementary protection to be provided by the owner. It is also important to understand clearly the extent of local public protection against theft, trespass, and vandalism. This section should also list the costs of any private custodial protection or protection against animal damage, windthrow, and other destructive forces that may be considered necessary.

V. *Capital improvement.* This includes land acquisition, planting, timber stand improvement, and other expenditures to increase total productivity. It also includes plans for roads, a home and office building, and other structural improvements such as bridges, equipment garages, and tool sheds, water supply, sewage disposal, and pond construction for fire protection and recreation.

VI. *Silvicultural plans.* Here should be outlined the measures to be taken to build up the quality and productivity of the forest and the care of forest stands.

VII. *Compartment descriptions and data.* This includes a general description and treatment for each compartment or logical subdivision of the property, its area, topography, soil, timber volume and quality, amount of silvicultural attention needed and date it should be done. It also includes tables showing the timber volume by species and diameter classes, the timber growth expected, fixed inventory plots to be established, and timber harvesting recommendations.

VIII. *Cutting budget.* This lists the amount of timber to be harvested each year by compartments and the anticipated revenue to be obtained. This cutting budget should be related to the long-term objective of attaining a more or less uniform annual yield; if an irregular yield is best suited to the owner's needs, the cutting budget should take recognition of this also.

IX. *Accounts and records.* Accounts and records are the tools by which the owner keeps account of the results of his management in terms of change in timber volume and quality, change in age-classes and stocking, and financial records of capital expenditures, income, and costs. Without satisfactory records, the owner is unable to determine whether his operations are financially successful and which operations are marginal or incurring losses.

X. *Ten-year financial plan.* The ten-year cutting budget lists the areas in which cutting will be done each year, or each two or three years, by compartment, and the volume of timber to be removed. The financial plan lists for each year the major expenditures anticipated for supplies, property taxes, interest, custodianship, and for forest management, in general, that embraces protection, timber stand improvement, and timber sale administration. Capital expenditures also should be listed for equipment, land acquisition, or major road construction. The question will often arise concerning whether a given expenditure should be listed as an operating expense or addition to capital. The Internal Revenue Service has guides on these questions that must be followed for taxation purposes.

The financial plan should also list anticipated revenue. This will include income from sale of timber, a part of which may be charged to depletion and, hence, is presumably available for reinvestment as capital, for leasing of hunting and fishing rights, for minor forest products, and for recreational privileges. This plan also should include additions to capital that the owner expects to make.

The ten-year plan should be summarized to show the financial expectation for the ten-year period.

A simplified management plan for a hypothetical property is presented later.

Information for Management Planning

From the preceding outline it is clear that certain basic information will be needed for management planning and decision making. Gaining this information will necessitate establishing operating units, obtaining timber growth rates, locating market outlets, deciding upon a permissible level of timber cutting, and determining cutting cycles and rotation.

Forestry as the management of land for commercial forest products has not been widely practiced by private landowners in the United States except by corporations or business owners engaged in the manufacture of lumber, paper, or other forest products. Forest management as an individual business enterprise, therefore, lacks the type of historical data and accounting record-keeping systems that a manual on farm management provides for the farmer, or one on retail merchandising brings to the prospective grocery store operator.

The forest owner necessarily will be pioneering in this aspect of his business enterprise.

Guiding concepts and suggestions offered here are devoted primarily to management of forest properties for timber crops. Owners do have widely varying objectives, however, and properties vary in their potential for management. Citations of sources of guidance for other objectives, such as forest recreational enterprises, are offered in the Bibliography.

Compartments, the Forest Operating Unit

A major forest property is usually divided, for the convenience of management, into a series of compartments that can serve as units for planning and record keeping. A compartment, the unit over which a timber operation would normally be carried out, may vary in area from 40 acres up to 500 acres in size, depending upon the total size of the property and the uniformity of the timber stand. For practical purposes, a 40-acre compartment would be about minimum in area, and a 300-acre compartment is about the maximum size for a 10,000-acre estate. Often the topography or existing roads help determine feasible compartments. Where the rectangular system of land survey exists, as in the central and western states, and topography and timber are uniform, the 40-acre or 160-acre blocks make satisfactory working units. In the thirteen original states, where a variety of land survey patterns prevail, the compartment may consist of an individual survey lot, or it may be an individual property acquisition, if not too large. The latter has many advantages because it is usually surveyed separately, has a separate timber inventory that was made at the time of acquisition, and probably also was managed as a unit by the previous owner. The new owner will find it useful to have a map of each compartment showing its boundaries with the compass bearings and lengths of the individual boundary lines. When the timber inventory is made, the timber cruise lines followed by the forester can be drawn on the maps, and roads and other features may be entered on the map as the inventory progresses. Such a compartment map will also include streams, ponds, open fields, and other features of note. Where other important topographic features exist, these, too, can be included on the map. The extra effort required to make a satisfactory map at the time of the timber inventory is not great, and the utility of such a map to the owner is high. Transferring compartment lines to air photos will also prove useful.

The Timber Inventory

A timber inventory should show the total volume of timber on each compartment separately, by species and diameter classes. Such a table is known as a "stand table." Small trees (ten to fifteen inches in diameter) increase in board foot volume much more rapidly, percentage-wise, with each unit increase in diameter than do large trees. For example, the board foot volume increases by 33 per cent as a tree grows from ten inches to eleven inches in diameter, but the volume increases by only 10 per cent as diameter increases from twenty inches to twenty-one inches. It is, therefore, generally best to have in mind a minimum diameter, such as sixteen inches, below which the better trees will be retained during early cutting operations. Also, it is difficult to market trees for logs that have not yet attained a minimum merchantable diameter of at least fifteen or sixteen inches. The stand table enables the owner quickly to determine the approximate harvest available above any diameter class.

The timber inventory also should give information on the age of the timber and time since the last cutting. Often the large trees left from a previous cutting years ago are so defecttive that they are practically worthless. The minimum amount of timber that it is profitable to harvest from a compartment will depend on the utility of existing roads, the size, species, and quality of the timber, the total volume to be cut, and average cut per acre. In the eastern United States, a minimum cut for sawtimber is generally considered to be approximately 1,500 to 2,000 board feet net volume per acre, depending on timber quality. A minimum cut for pulpwood is about seven cords per acre. If the timber operator must build his own roads and if he must log steep or rocky slopes, the cut will have to be increased considerably above this minimum to make the operation feasible.

The Timber Growth Rate

The financial success of forest management depends basically on the timber growth rate. Thus the owner should have a reasonably accurate estimate of how fast the timber on his estate is increasing in volume and value. Determining growth rate accurately for a forest property is one of the most challenging tasks of forestry. Growth can be estimated either by comparing the increase in merchantable volume, as measured on similar stands, with the timber stand in question, or by projecting past and current growth of the stand into the future. Various tables are available from forestry schools and public forest experiment stations giving information on growth. These can also be found in the *Forestry Handbook.* [1] Most growth information is general in nature and should be adjusted to meet the conditions of the individual stand. Making such an adjustment is a task for an experienced forester, though the owner himself can gradually develop some ability in this area. If the owner does not want to have a professional job done, he can use general growth data that may be had from the state forester. Local public foresters can also give him a general guide for expected growth.

The growth rate in board feet for a stand of timber varies considerably with size and age and quality of the growing site. A mature stand in which losses are occurring because of windthrow, disease, or insect depredations may have no net growth; it may, in fact, be declining in timber volume. A

young stand just below sawtimber size also has no measure-
able growth in board feet. As soon as young trees do reach
minimum merchantable size, the growth rate in percentage of
existing board foot volume is very high. This rate of volume
increase for the stand progressively declines as all the trees in
the stand attain board foot size, and continues to decline as
the volume base increases with increasing age. Growth rates
up to 10 per cent or more may occur in pine stands having an
average diameter of ten inches. For stands with average diameters of twenty-four inches, this growth rate would probably
be nearer 4 per cent, though total board foot growth would
usually be more than for the ten-inch stand. The growth rate
also can be increased by periodic thinning as the trees increase
in size. An example of a simplified and abbreviated local
growth table is given in Table 4.

TABLE 4
LOCAL GROWTH TABLE FOR WHITE PINE IN NEW YORK STATE*

Gross volume per acre (board feet)	Average growth per acre per year (board feet)	Growth (per cent)
1,000	250	25
3,000	400	13
5,000	500	10
7,000	600	9
9,000	700	8
11,000	750	7
13,000	750	5
15,000	725	5
17,000	700	4

*Adapted from Miles J. Ferree and Robert P. Hagar, *Timber Growth Rates for Natural Forest Stands in New York State,* State University of New York College of Forestry, Syracuse, *Technical Bulletin 78,* 1956.

From Table 4 it may be seen that little advantage accrues in
holding a greater growing stock than 9,000 board feet, when

rate of return on the growing stock investment, as well as relative risk carried, is important to the owner.

The most precise method of determining growth is to measure every tree on the forest property at the beginning of a period and then repeat the process five or ten years later. This is a very time-consuming and costly operation, even for a property as small as 100 acres, and is quite infeasible for one of 1,000 acres or larger. A substitute method of reasonable accuracy is to establish fixed inventory plots to be periodically remeasured. These plots might be one-fifth acre in size, circular in shape, and each tree should be numbered and measured. Five years later these same trees can be remeasured by number and a precise determination of mortality and of growth of each tree and the total for the area of the plot obtained. Sufficient plots are required to give a reliable average for the forest. This method, too, is rather costly to establish because of the need for permanency and detail. Other methods of obtaining growth information are likely to overestimate the growth potential of a property. The aid of consulting foresters should be sought in establishing such fixed inventory plots, but once they have been established, the owner himself may be able to remeasure them periodically and keep his information current.

Market Outlets

In the earlier discussion of the preliminary examination of an area to be selected for a forest holding, emphasis was placed on the importance of markets for timber. More precise information should be obtained after the property is actually acquired. The market for both pulpwood and sawtimber is likely to fluctuate widely from year to year. Also, the market for hardwoods as opposed to softwoods will vary considerably. The owner should get a list of stumpage buyers and log buyers within hauling distance of his property, find out the kinds of products purchased, the specifications for these, the current prices paid, and the quantities purchased annually. If he anticipates having a substantial volume to sell each year, he may be able to bargain for preferred arrangements with buyers concerning both volume and price and reach commitments on acceptable delivery times.

He will need to line up a reliable logger covered by compensation insurance on whom he can depend to handle his timber cutting acceptably on a marked-tree basis.

Establishing an Allowable or Permissible Level of Cutting

Since usable timber can grow only on trees of merchantable size, the owner will wish to build up his timber growing stock to a volume that brings a reasonably high income per acre. In Table 4, a white pine stand having 9,000 board feet per acre would grow 700 board feet per year. A further growing stock volume increase to 17,000 board feet per acre increases growth very little. Beyond this, mortality takes a heavy toll. However, inasmuch as many carrying charges are related to area rather than to timber volume, a moderately high growing stock volume may prove more profitable, particularly where growth is good. The owner will, therefore, decide upon what he considers to be an optimum amount of growing stock to carry as an average capital investment per acre for a rate of return he deems reasonable on that investment, and also the interval of time over which he hopes to achieve that volume. Knowing his annual growth rate, he can add this to his present volume and in this way determine how much can be harvested over a ten-year period and still leave enough accrued growth on the remaining stand to meet his long-term timber stocking objective. Most of the forested land that can be acquired is understocked and has too many trees of poor quality standing on the land that have been rejected in earlier logging operations. It is well to harvest such trees, if merchantable, early in the management operations so that better quality trees can be grown in their space. For this reason it may be desirable to postpone the date at which optimum timber stocking is to be obtained, because there is little point in carrying a large volume of low-quality trees which may be deteriorating rather than increasing in value. A conservative approach is to cut approximately half of the growth over the first ten-year period and gradually to increase the amount cut as the desired stocking volume is approached. Thereafter, the annual cuts may average the same as the annual net growth. Usually professional help is needed to determine what the effects of various levels of cutting are likely to be on volume accumulation.

In Table 5 a simplified example, based upon growth data from Table 4, is given for a compartment of eastern white pine.

TABLE 5
CUMULATIVE GROWTH FOR EASTERN WHITE PINE

	First decade	Second decade	Third decade	Fourth decade to end of rotation
Volume at start (board feet acre)	3,000	5,000	7,000	9,000
Growth during decade	4,000	5,000	6,000	7,000
Total available by end of decade	7,000	10,000	13,000	16,000
Cut at end of decade	2,000	3,000	4,000	7,000
Volume after cutting	5,000	7,000	9,000	9,000

The owner, in this case, achieves his goal of 9,000 board feet per acre at the end of the third decadal cutting cycle. There is little advantage in his aspiring for a higher volume, since maximum practical growth rate would be attained at about this degree of stocking. He might consider shortening his cutting cycle to some five to eight years after achieving his optimum degree of stocking in the hopes of increasing total growth rate slightly.

The Cutting Cycle

The cutting cycle, or interval between cuts, is determined by the growth rate and by the minimum amount of harvestable timber required to make a stumpage sale commercially feasible. The length of time to achieve optimum stocking must also be considered. In the pine example presented in Table 5, by expecting a minimum cut of 2,000 board feet per acre and annual growth of 400 board feet per acre, and harvesting approximately half the annual growth, the cutting cycle turns out to be ten years. The shorter the cutting cycle, the more completely may the owner expect to harvest all the timber that is produced. If a long cutting cycle must be adopted, he can expect to lose several trees by mortality between the two cutting dates. Once the growing stock is built up to a point where the annual growth can be removed, a cutting cycle of ten years or less can usually be adopted.

Rotation

A forest rotation is the cycle of time between timber stand establishment and final stand harvest. In even-aged stand management, common with pine and other conifers and certain hardwoods, all trees remaining in the stand at that time are harvested and a new crop started. For aspen, southern pine, and short-lived species, this "rotation age" would probably be fifty years or slightly less. For white pine, it may be eighty to one hundred years, and for sugar maple and other long-lived trees, as much as one hundred fifty to two hundred years. Unless a timber stand is already well advanced at the time the forest area is purchased, the rotation is rarely completed within the lifetime of the owner. This emphasizes the need both for careful investment planning and for having the continuity of a timber management plan. Obviously, with a long rotation, a number of intermediate harvest cuttings are made. It is sometimes desirable to start the young stand long before the last of the old trees are removed, in which case the rotation is less important than tree size and cutting cycle. These old trees, if of fine quality for veneer purposes, will increase in value at a rapid rate after their competitors have been removed, and they provide a certain amount of shade and shelter for the young crop. If held too long, however, they are sure to suppress the young trees, and they can cause heavy damage when felled. In some cases, it may be desirable to carry a few trees much longer than the normal rotation. They can then be removed as high-quality veneer logs at the time the younger trees are harvested as sawlogs or pulpwood, thereby limiting the damage.

A Sample Management Plan

The remainder of this chapter is devoted to describing a simplified hypothetical management plan for the years 1967-77. This plan represents what could occur on a 4,000-acre property in the eastern United States. The values in the tables, though within normal ranges, should not be considered as indicative of how any specific forest property might work out financially. It illustrates the kind of information and the sort of records that are needed to project a management plan.

General Locality

Highland Forest, located in the central region of the northeastern United States, is forty-five miles from the prosperous and growing city of Pinetum, which has a population of 100,000 and a diversified industrial pattern. Several smaller cities and villages with important industries are within the forty-five-mile radius. A pulpmill is located at Woodville, thirty miles distant, a veneer mill at Pinetum, and five local sawmills operate within a fifteen-mile hauling distance of Highland Forest. The region near the forest is well supplied with all-weather highways, and two town-maintained roads cross the property. Agriculture has retreated from the land above 1,200 feet elevation and also from the less productive soils in the valleys and on the slopes. The soils, generally, support good hardwood timber in the areas not formerly cleared for agriculture.

The topography is a dissected plateau with broad valleys of generally good agricultural land, moderately steep slopes generally pastured or abandoned to forest, and plateau lands above 1,200 feet elevation, mostly in forest or in the process of returning to forest.

The region was settled 150 years ago, and timber operations passed their peak in 1860, with agriculture reaching its peak in 1900. Second- and third-growth forest, occupying about 60 per cent of the land area, supports an important, but not very prosperous, wood-based economy. The region is dependent on timber imports for 70 per cent of local needs. Timber operators are present but vary in reliability. Since agriculture is still declining, the region has an adequate labor supply. County and school taxes average about $0.40 per acre per year. The increase during the past decade has averaged $0.04 per acre. Other sources of taxable wealth in the county carry the main tax burden. The local citizenry are law abiding, and damage from malicious mischief or trespass other than for hunting has been insignificant for forest properties. The county board of supervisors is sympathetic toward summer residents and encourages sheriff protection.

The owner, Mr. Philodendron, age thirty-six years, is a junior partner in a prosperous law firm in Pinetum. He has several important industrial accounts, and his hours tend to be rather long, though he has considerable flexibility in planning his work day. He has a minor health difficulty that has caused his physician to recommend outdoor activities as a relief from office pressure. He has been spending many of his weekends as well as his one-month vacation on the property, living in a farmhouse he has renovated for use during the summer months. He has a family of four children, the oldest ten years of age,

A farmhouse acquired with a forest property can sometimes be used as a temporary residence. Eventually an owner will want and need a residence with more conveniences and esthetic appeal than many such houses afford.

and an understanding wife who shares his desire for outdoor life. Mr. Philodendron has always had a love of the forest and open country, so began three years ago to acquire the Highland Forest property.

His original objective was to acquire a place for summer living and for personal and family recreation. As he began buying properties, the possibilities of making it also a profitable investment began to intrigue him, adding new interest to the venture. He recognized that this required careful planning, and he drew up the following list of objectives for his forest estate:

1) To afford summer and weekend recreation for himself and his family.

2) To provide an investment for surplus funds. The property was purchased from savings.

3) To provide a year-round residence from age fifty-six onward when he expects to relinquish full-time partnership responsibilities.

4) Since Mr. Philodendron has ample income to meet family needs and expects this to continue to be the case, net income from the property is not a major consideration; rather he wishes to build up the capital value of the property by allowing growth to accumulate on the best quality trees. This will then serve as a form of insurance in that high-quality timber will become increasingly available to provide income for retirement years or earlier, should his health deteriorate so that a regular work schedule can no longer be maintained.

5) He would like the property to afford his children an opportunity for personal earnings to supply their spending money and some of their college expenses. For this purpose, he has in mind selling Christmas greens and wreaths, pine cones, and berries as possible means of affording work in which children can engage that may bring in some income. He also expects to use his youngsters to do such light work as running compass lines, tallying trees, applying silvicides to

girdled trees, shearing Christmas trees, and painting boundary lines. As the children get older, they can help cut fuelwood and pulpwood. Since the amount of such work that will be performed is uncertain, he has not incorporated it separately in his management plan.

6) Mr. Philodendron has found the forest retreat to be a place where he can spend his summer mornings in various legal business and his afternoons with his children on forest work. He therefore has the added benefit of lengthening his weekends with but little sacrifice to professional activity.

With the help of Mr. Sylva, his consulting forester whom he employed to appraise the timber and growth possibilities of each lot, he incorporated the above objectives into the management plan.

Description of Property

Highland Forest Estate is made up of ten major parcels and eight minor ones totaling 4,075 acres. It is bounded roughly by Cross Hill Road, Spring Valley Road, Pioneer Ridge Trail, and Coon Creek. It includes the area known locally as Magner's Hill. Elevations are from 800 to 1,600 feet.

The property has been divided into fifteen compartments (see Figure 8). The timber volume in 1966 totaled 9,610,000 board feet, and the total annual growth was 795,000 board feet made up of mixed pine and hardwoods.

Mr. Philodendron has marked out the general boundaries of his property on the Spring Valley U.S. Geological Survey contour map and also on the Woodville County map. He has also purchased aerial photographs on which the individual compartment boundary lines have been traced. Compartment maps were furnished by Mr. Sylva as a part of the appraisal made before the individual lots were purchased. Mr. Sylva reported that the soil generally, though stony, is of medium to good quality for timber growth. Scattered rock outcrops are found on the ridges which offer scenic overlooks of interest for rec-

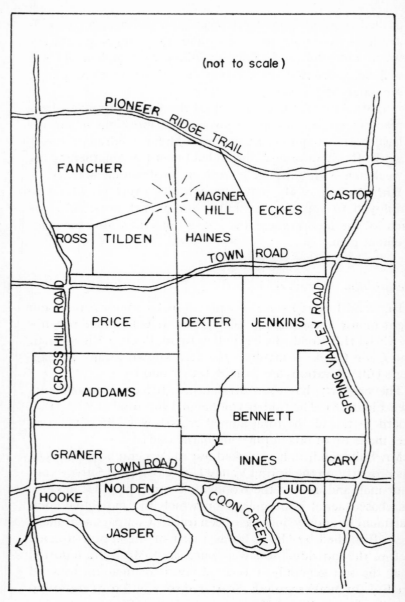

Sketch map of Highland Forest Property.

reational use. A small brook flows from the property into Coon Creek. Along the brook and in several other locations, sites are available for erecting dams for small ponds. Although Mr. Philodendron owns frontage along Coon Creek, the fishing rights had been leased to the state for public use before he acquired the property. Some open land is used by his custodian, a local farmer, for pasture as a part of his compensation. Access is available to all lots from public roads, old rights-of-way, or over property Mr. Philodendron now owns. He plans to open the old roads for use in forest operations and for recreational use, though he does not intend to make them inviting to passenger cars.

Upland game, grouse, pheasant, deer, cottontail rabbits, and gray squirrels are common. Woodcock are found along Coon Creek. Other animals of interest include raccoon, woodchuck, snowshoe hare, porcupine, a few mink and fox, skunks, and opossum. Birds are those of the northern and transition forest—scarlet tanager, ovenbird, wood thrush, olive-back thrush, catbird, towhee, goldfinch, chickadee, nuthatch, crow, bluejay, various hawks and owls, indigo bunting, and many others. The forest is attractive to fall and winter migrants, of which the warblers are of interest. Mrs. Philodendron enjoys bird watching and has interested her eldest daughter.

Protection

Protection against fire is provided by the state, with three fire towers that overlook the property. The state has a good division of pest control that provides protection against insects and diseases. The custodian's son, who enjoys hunting and trapping, keeps the area free from excessive damage by porcupines and other animals. He also keeps an eye on the camp and stays alert for timber trespass.

Capital Improvement

The owner plans no major capital improvement during the

first decade but does have in mind increasing the area to 5,000 acres or more. He expects to do some Christmas tree planting and timber stand improvement but intends to finance these activities as a part of current operations.

Silvicultural Plans

The owner wishes to remove most of the overmature and defective trees during the first ten-year cutting cycle. His objective is to build up the growing stock to 9,000 board feet per acre on his pine lands and 6,000 on his hardwood lands. He anticipates a rotation age of one hundred years for both softwoods and hardwoods.

Compartment Descriptions

Addams compartment, two hundred acres. The Addams compartment comprises all of lot 47, Monroe Hill Patent. The land is all good site on slopes between 1,000 and 1,300 feet elevation. Slopes are moderate and moisture is prevalent. The timber stand volume is given in Table 6. The total volume is

TABLE 6
STAND VOLUME IN ADDAMS COMPARTMENT (200 ACRES) IN 1965
Highland Forest Estate

Diameter Class (inches)	Volume in thousand board feet				
	Total	Maple	Beech	Pine	Oak
10	40	30	. . . .	10	. . . .
12	100	50	20	20	10
14	135	50	35	35	15
16	135	45	35	30	25
18	140	45	50	25	20
20	130	20	70	10	30
22	80	30	50	. . . .	. . . .
24	40	. . . .	30	. . . .	10
Total	800	270	290	130	110

800,000 board feet, or an average of 4,000 board feet per acre. The annual growth is 60,000 board feet. Permanent inventory plots 10 to 20 are located on this compartment. Part of the volume is in overmature beech which should be removed early in the life of the property. Various cull trees also are present that should be eliminated by use of silvicides. An open field of ten acres is suitable for machine planting.

The stand in question is low in volume in the small and large diameter classes but relatively high in volume in the middle diameter classes. From an examination of this table, the owner decides that he can afford to cut all beech eighteen inches and larger in diameter and most of the pine, oak, and maple twenty inches and larger in diameter. With a stumpage value of $15.00 for beech, pine, and oak and $40.00 for maple, the total amount realized in the cut would be approximately $5,750.

Similar descriptive material and detailed data should be prepared on the other fourteen compartments.

Cutting Budget

The owner wishes during the first cutting cycle to harvest half the growth so that a higher total volume may be harvested in succeeding cycles. After studying his compartment inventories and growth tables, he decides on the cutting plan outlined in Table 7.

Note that Table 7 shows by compartments the area, the year in which the cutting is expected, the annual growth, the initial timber volume, the volume that would be available at the time of cutting, estimates of the volume to be cut, and the anticipated income. For a 4,075-acre tract, this plan projects an average annual cut of 338,000 board feet, bringing in an average income of $5,505, or $1.35 per acre per year.

The owner draws up a prospectus and tentative contract for the first year's cutting and advertises for competitive bids from timber operators and other interested stumpage buyers.

TABLE 7
TEN-YEAR CUTTING PLAN
Highland Forest Estate

Compartment	Area (acres)	Year to cut	Annual Growth MBF*	Timber Volume MBF*		Volume to cut MBF*	Anticipated Income (dollars)
				1966	At cutting year		
Addams	200	1966	60	800	800	300	5750
Bennett	400	1967	80	1200	1280	420	5040
Cary	60	1968	10	240	260	80	1120
Castor	120	1968	20	400	440	150	2250
Dexter	280	1969	80	900	1140	280	5040
Eckes	310	1970	80	1000	1320	420	7140
Fancher	480	1971	90	1000	1450	450	7200
Graner	220	1972	70	900	1320	430	8600
Haines	325	1973	70	1050	1540	430	6450
Innes	210	1974	60	420	900	320	5260
Jenkins	300	1975	30	300	570	100	1200
Others	1170	1976	125	1400	....	....	....
Total for Decade	4075	....	795	9610	....	3380	55050

*MBF, forester's abbreviation for one thousand board feet.

Accounts and Records

The owner decides on keeping an accurate record of the following:

1) the timber volume cut and receipts therefrom, by compartments

2) the growth at five-year intervals as revealed by fixed inventory plots

3) the change in total timber volume, as revealed by a new timber cruise, or by depletions and growth, at the end of ten years

4) the annual income from timber sales and all other sources

5) annual costs segregated into the following classes—

Fixed costs:
Land taxes
Custodial fees
Maintenance of roads, boundaries, etc.
Administration costs

Variable costs:
Silvicultural costs such as thinning, removing cull trees, and caring for plantations

Timber sale costs:
Tree marking and sale administration
Equipment amortization
Inventories and growth information

Capital investments:
Land purchases
Acquisition costs
Plantations
Permanent roads and improvements
Depletion

6) the total costs and income and change in capital value over the ten-year period.

He expects to prepare annual budgets and annual financial operating statements and a balance sheet.

The Ten-Year Operating Budget

The ten-year operating budget is summarized in Table 8. Taxes, custodial fees, and other fixed charges are estimated to increase from $3,200 to $3,700 during the ten-year period. The income listed represents gross income from stumpage sales for the year, less cost of sale. The improvement operations represent expenditures that are expected to yield returns in later decades, but not in the initial ten-year period.

TABLE 8
PROJECTED TEN-YEAR OPERATING BUDGET
Highland Forest Estate

Year	Operation	Cost of opera- tion	Taxes & other fixed charges	Total costs	Esti- mated income	Profit (or Loss)
1966	Planting 30 acres	$ 600	$ 3,200	$ 3,800	$ 4,740	$ 1,950
1967	Planting 40 acres	800	3,250	4,050	5,040	990
1968	Thinning 35 acres	700	3,300	4,000	3,370	(630)
1969	Pruning 30 acres	300	3,300	3,600	5,040	1,440
1970	Plantation care, 70 acres	700	3,400	4,100	7,140	3,040
1971	Boundary marking and measuring inventory plots	600	3,400	4,000	7,200	3,200
1972	Timber stand improve- ment, 150 acres	1,500	3,500	5,000	8,600	3,600
1973	Timber stand improve- ment, 100 acres	1,000	3,500	4,500	6,450	1,950
1974	Pruning 40 acres	400	3,600	4,000	5,260	1,260
1975	Re-inventory and management plan	2,500	3,700	6,200	1,200	(5,000)
	Totals	$9,100	$34,150	$43,250	$54,040	$11,800

It should be noted that Mr. Philodendron has planned to make but modest annual expenditures for forest improvement measures. He expects, instead, to use his capital first to expand his holdings in the anticipation that land values may increase substantially by the end of the decade.

It should also be noted that no fee is charged for supervision and management. Mr. Philodendron expects to assume this task himself as a part of his personal pleasure in owning the property. Travel costs are considered to be offset by family recreation the property affords.

Mr. Philodendron has considered leasing hunting and fishing rights and also leasing camp- and homesites, but decided against any such usage in the immediate future. He prefers to have the exclusive use of the property. Later he plans to open his property to a few personal friends and associates for recreational use, on a shared-cost basis. This will involve developing a pond suitable for fishing and bathing and camps suitable for guest occupancy.

Table 9 illustrates the expected return from the property over the initial ten-year period and the change in net worth. The results of Mr. Philodendron's operation are a net income of $11,800 and an increase in timber inventory of $44,700, or a total increase in value of $56,500. This is equivalent to 4.7 per cent average interest for the period. Actually, the percentage return is somewhat higher as income was received throughout the period. A forest owner who made as good a showing as this during his first ten years would have cause to congratulate himself. He would have laid the base for better growth and higher returns in the following decades.

TABLE 9
CHANGE IN NET WORTH, 1966-75
Highland Forest Estate

	1966	1975
Land (4,075 acres @ $5 per acre)	$ 20,375	$ 20,375
Timber (@ $10 per MBF)		
1966 (9,610 MBF)	96,100	
1975 (13,580 MBF)		135,800
Plantations (70 acres @ $20)		1,400
Pruning at cost		700
Thinning at cost		700
Timber stand improvement at cost		2,500
Net investment and growth increment	44,700	
Totals	$161,175	$161,175

The advantage in making a projection of this type is that the investor is warned in advance of the types of expenditures he might anticipate incurring so that he can make appropriate adjustments. He might, for example, prefer a different distribution of income from that shown. If at the end of the sixth year his son will be going away to college, he might prefer to defer his income until this period and concentrate his cutting during the four years his son would be in school. While this might be good financial management for the family, it would delay the conversion of the property from an understocked forest having a high percentage of low-value trees to a more thriftily growing and productive forest. An individual would be obliged to make his choices accordingly. During his initial ten-year operating period, he might well wish to be somewhat conservative on investment-type expenses until he determines whether or not his income is going to cover operating costs. Modification in his management plan could be made at the end of five years, after he had had an opportunity to check his timber growth rates from permanent inventory plots and to test the market through timber sales.

Summary

Forest management covers those activities in which an owner engages to achieve his objectives for his forest property. Management produces both public and private benefits. Well carried out timber operations can improve the quality of future harvests and, at the same time, augment the value of the property for water yield, recreation, and use by wildlife.

A management plan is an orderly outline for development and use of a forest. Its preparation requires the personal attention of the owner, for it is his specific forest estate, and the plan is directed at meeting his individual aims and wishes.

A forest estate is more easily managed when divided into logical planning parcels, or compartments, that serve as management units. Timber inventories, cutting plans, and other operations are then planned and scheduled by compartments.

The annual cut may be determined by the owner, depending upon the condition of the forest and the rate at which he expects to achieve full growing stock. Cutting cycles depend upon growth rate and minimum volumes essential for a commercial cut. Rotation is the interval between final harvest cuts. The rotation should be long enough to attain optimum mean annual income.

A hypothetical plan for management of a forest property is given, illustrating methods and interrelationships that enter into management planning decisions.

Literature Cited

1. Reginald D. Forbes and Arthur B. Meyer, *Forestry Handbook* (New York: Ronald Press, 1955), Sec. 1, pp. 90-98.

 VI

Timber Marketing

The most feasible way for the owner to improve his forest property is through the sale of timber, provided cutting is concentrated on the lower-value trees. Few owners have either the time or the necessary skill and equipment to do their own logging. Contracting with woods operators to buy, cut, and remove standing trees as specified by the owner is the standard and accepted procedure for selling merchantable timber. Standing timber sold in this manner is referred to as "stumpage." While the contractor, in such cases, is interested only in the salable volume that he can derive in the form of logs and pulpwood, the owner can exercise considerable practical control over the quality, species, and location of trees removed and minimize the damage to the residual stand by the way the sale is made and the type of contract to which he agrees.

It is by cutting timber that the owner is able to make his impress on the forest. Thereby he can transform the growth from poor-quality to good-quality trees. By removing overmature trees, he can make full use of his land area and maintain his timber growing stock in vigorous condition. He can improve the appearance of his forest while also increasing the interest yield on his investment. Thus, cutting considerations are important whether the owner holds his land primarily for the personal satisfaction it brings or holds it as an asset for continuous income production.

Locating a Market

The forest owner should seek the help of his local state

132

district forester or county forester before making a timber sale. Either official can suggest reliable consulting foresters in the area and advise if their services should be sought. The local forester will probably be well acquainted with markets and with the loggers, sawmill operators, veneer mill operators, and pulp and paper companies, and he can generally help arrange contact with their timber agents.

A visit to some of the main timber-using mills or ultimate log buyers will generally be helpful. Although in some cases the owner may not deal with buyers directly, they can provide firsthand information on market specifications and should know the names of loggers and be able to offer advice concerning their reliability. Also, in cases where the forest owner is managing a sizable property for long-term timber production, the better mills will be interested in helping build toward stability in timber use since they will look forward to purchasing logs and pulpwood from the property for a number of years to come. They can give accurate information on the prices of logs of various grades and provide a range of applicable logging and hauling costs, which will help the landowner in bargaining with the logger.

Kinds of Timber Sales

Standing timber may be sold in several ways: by the tract, by selling all trees above a given diameter limit, by selling as a part of a land-clearing operation, and by selling on a marked-tree basis. If the tract is sold for a lump sum, the logger, unless other directions are given, will remove all the trees he considers merchantable. He will leave the culls and small trees standing, many of which may be broken over or otherwise injured in his logging operations. In other words, such a sale is by logger's choice. The owner has thereby, wittingly or not, given away control over the future of his investment, and he may incur more damage than income. Logger's choice is usually least advantageous to the long-term forest owner unless he wishes the land cleared to start a new crop or for other purposes. Such a cutting usually results in a devastated forest.

The one major advantage to the owner of selling a tract for a lump sum is that he knows what he is to receive and can demand payment in advance, thereby avoiding, in some states, liability for workmen's compensation claims in the event of accident to the logger or his men. However, this type of sale is preferred and sought by the logger, for he is then free to operate as he pleases and usually does so. Trees he considers to be of questionable value are left standing. Also, the buyer is usually much more aware of both standing merchantable volume and value than the owner, even in the absence of an accurate measurement, and discounts his offer amply to cover any errors or contingencies. Furthermore, neither he nor the owner can be sure just how the logs will look after they have been cut from the tree. If defects hidden in the tree show up when the logs are cut, the buyer of the standing tree has received something less than he expected. He will generally make liberal allowance for such defects. Since the owner also lacks accurate information on the probable net volume in the tract, and is less experienced in estimates, markets, and quality than the logger, the advantage lies heavily with the logger.

A diameter limit cut may bring just as much return as a logger's choice and, in addition, help reserve the smaller trees for future growth. However, this, too, is seldom the most satisfactory to the landowner since it tends to leave the less vigorous trees for future crop trees. There are some cases where such a sale is suitable. It works well for harvesting short-lived species such as aspen or jack pine and may be advisable for making a first cut in an old field stand of white pine. Usually the larger trees, in this latter case, are those that are badly weeviled and have coarse limbs and, hence, are least desirable for future crop trees. Again, however, the owner has placed much of his forest's future in the hands of the logger.

The land clearing sale such as an owner would make on an area he expected to flood for a small lake or pond requires the removal of all the trees and is likely to net the owner considerably less than sale of merchantable trees by tract at logger's choice. Many small unmerchantable trees must be cut and removed or burned on the site. This is a costly operation. In some localities, however, it is possible to sell the smaller material to a pulpwood or fuelwood operator who can utilize it.

The marked-tree sale is the type ordinarily to be preferred. In this kind of sale the owner or his agent marks the trees that are to be cut and specifies penalties for cutting unmarked trees. Forked and limby trees, those bearing evidence of disease, those that have been injured by fire or past logging, and those of inferior species should be cut first. From the logger's standpoint, this is the least desirable type of sale because he must cut the low-value trees and leave many of the higher-value ones. Usually the sale will include a careful selection of some of the better trees as well, as a part of sound timber management, but also to make the whole operation financially attractive to both logger and owner. This kind of sale can often be made without any sacrifice to the long-term development of the timber stand. For example, if crop trees have been selected, cutting a large tree that is interfering with the crop tree is normally the best thing to do. The small trees that are unprofitable to log can be left for a later cut. A skilled timber marker will know about what the logger can afford to do, and he will try to mark the trees in such a way that the future stand will develop satisfactorily and the logger will obtain enough good trees along with the poorer ones to make his total operation profitable. The forest owner, therefore, should employ the services of a consultant, or at least seek advice from the state district forester, when available, for his first marking operation. It is well for the owner to go with the forester as he marks the trees and from time to time discuss with him why certain trees are marked and others left. In this way he can gain some familiarity with the art of selective cutting that must integrate forest growth considerations with marketing reality. Equally important, in this way the

An owner watches while his forester marks trees for cutting.

owner can also get some idea of the lower limits of physical and financial operating feasibility for the logger on that tract.

As he marks the trees for sale, the tree marker usually keeps a running record, by species, of diameter, number of logs, and estimated amount of defect in percentage of volume. This enables him to draw up an estimate of the total volume of timber by species to be offered in the timber sale. Where quality is good enough to warrant selling on grade, the estimate should also show approximate grade percentages. This is especially helpful if the sale is to be offered at public bid. When the trees that are to be sold are marked, they can be sold either on the measured volume as they stand (tree measurement sale) with no further measurement after they are cut, or they can be sold by number of trees with the net sale volume determined by log scale (scaled sale) as the logs are removed. When timber quality is marginal, the scaled volume, with a percentage deduction estimated for defect, is a fairer basis for settlement for both owner and operator than gross volume.

If the logger is obliged to pay only for the logs as they are scaled at the mill, he is taking no risk of paying for timber he cannot sell. Cull logs can be left in the woods, as they would be anyhow. The owner gets paid on the quantity of material sold and removed, and the logger for the products he delivers. On the other hand, this places both the logger and the owner at the mercy of the mill scaler and mill specifications, and provides the mill with little incentive for careful utilization.

If choice logs and species are among those purchased and if a veneer mill or loading center is nearby, the logger will probably sort out such logs and sell them in that market at much higher prices. Unless a separate price is specified for veneer logs, or for specialty species such as white ash, the same stumpage price per thousand board feet applies as for ordinary sawlogs. The timber buyer usually has a canny eye for trees that will meet veneer or other market specifications, and takes the quantity of suitable logs into consideration in his bid for the timber offered. In some parts of the country, logs are currently being bought at the sawmill on a log-grade basis. Log grading is still less precise than lumber grading and is not too widely practiced. Where logs are bought at the mill on grade, the forest owner might well consider specifying different prices for log grades one, two, and three by species.

Log Rules

Logs are bought and sold on the basis of their measured scale, according to the log rule in local use in the region. The several different kinds of rules vary considerably in the volumes they give for logs of various sizes. Therefore, it is advisable that the forest owner understand something about them. The rule to be used should always be specified in a timber contract, along with the specifications of what constitutes a minimum merchantable log to be scaled as part of the sold volume.

A log rule is a simple measurement device with a table of numbers specifying the board foot contents that can be sawn from logs of various diameters and lengths. If a log is defective, the extent of the defect is scaled by the same rule, and this amount is deducted from the total scale volume. Complexity enters with the numbers of different log rules in use. Many of them give an underestimate of the lumber volume that will be sawn from a log, with the overrun varying mostly with log diameter. A forest owner actually sells trees, rather than logs. Tree volumes are usually considerably underevaluated in terms of lumber that can be cut from them if sold on the scale given by certain widely used log rules. Table 10 illustrates how much the differences in board foot volume can be when applied to a twelve-inch and a twenty-four-inch tree, each having two and one-half logs, sixteen feet long.

The International Log Rule has been developed from diagrams and checked against actual lumber yield from sawing logs. If careful sawing is applied, this log rule will provide a measure of the lumber that may be obtained within plus or

TABLE 10
DIFFERENCES IN LOG RULES

Log Rule	12-inch tree board feet	24-inch tree board feet
International	78	408
Scribner	60	374
Doyle	30	318

minus 2 per cent accuracy. Because of its lack of overrun, this rule is not popular with sawmill operators and for this reason may not be in use by those to whom a local logger is obliged to make his deliveries. The owner, therefore, usually finds it necessary to sell on the basis of the log rules currently in use in his neighborhood, irrespective of whether they favor the log buyer. Actually, sawmill men are acquainted with the overrun to be expected and take this into account in the price they offer. Similarly, the logger automatically adjusts to the differences, often buying timber on one log rule and selling on one or more other log rules. Stumpage prices offered vary accordingly, but not necessarily proportionately to differences in log rule volumes. The landowner is the one who is usually unaware, at his expense.

There is another factor to be considered from the sawmill men's viewpoint. It costs considerably more per thousand board feet to saw lumber from small logs than large ones, and both quality and value of lumber sawn is higher from larger logs; hence, the mill operator is justified in paying a lower unit price for the small ones than the large ones. If the logs are graded, the grading rules themselves attempt to take this into account, but if the logs are not graded, the Doyle Rule, despite its inaccuracy, gives a closer approximation of the real value of the log to the sawmill man on a flat rate per thousand than does the International Rule. Hence, it may not be as unfair to the timber owner and logger as it seems.

Detailed information on log rules and log scaling is available in *Forestry Handbook,*[1] Section 1. Local foresters can also supply information for the guidance of timberland owners.

Choosing a Timber Operator

Many methods may be followed by the owner in selecting an operator to cut his timber. An estimate of the volume of timber offered for sale may be prepared and sent to loggers and bids requested. If the timber is choice and offered in considerable volume, it may be possible to attract three or more bidders on the sale. The owner will then select the highest bidder, or if he has reason to reject a logging operator's bid, select the second or third highest.

The second method is to contract directly with the sawmill or pulp company. These companies will usually subcontract with the logger who performs the operation on the ground. In this system the logger is responsible to his employer, the mill, rather than to the owner, and is likely to be less responsive to the owner's wishes than if he contracts directly with the owner. On the other hand, the mill owner is likely to be more reliable to deal with than the logger.

A third method is to contract directly with the logger as the result of negotiation. This method has much merit for the well-informed forest owner. It gives him an opportunity to investigate several loggers and to select the one whom he deems to be the most reliable and the most responsive to his wishes. It offers advantages to the logger, for if he pleases the owner with the quality of his dealings, he can be assured of repeated sales in the future without the necessity of negotiating each time with a new owner. It has the further advantage of aiding in establishing a good owner-logger relationship since, because the owner is interested in maintaining a good logger, he will not press unduly for a price advantage at each individual sale but will seek to make his dealings fair to the logger as well as to himself. If the owner tries to be too sharp in his dealings, he may lose his logger and have to find another. If a reliable logger is found, a general contract can be drawn up that may be extended from year to year and from compartment to compartment to follow the owner's cutting plan.

Logs of fuelwood or pulpwood size can be handled with a light tractor and truck. Such light equipment is unsuitable, however, for handling sawtimber.

The fourth method is for the owner to run the logging operation himself by hiring piece cutters, a skidder, and a hauler. This has certain advantages in that the owner then realizes the profit of the logging operation as well as from the stumpage. He also gets experience in logging and thereby becomes better acquainted with the relative profitability of cutting trees of various sizes. If he is prepared to make a major investment himself, he can actually hire the loggers on an hourly basis, have them operate his own equipment, and thereby realize the full advantage of the logging operation. For various reasons, however, this is not a recommended practice. In either case, the owner must be prepared to give considerable personal attention to on-the-job details, and he must keep adequate records and provide accident compensation coverage and other insurance to protect himself. This can be costly in both time and money, particularly for the inexperienced.

The method to follow in choosing a timber operator will depend both on the owner's property (the size, character, and the amount of timber available for sale) and the frequency of sales as well as on the amount of time that the owner personally can devote to supervising the operations and the amount of capital he is prepared to invest in logging equipment. Whatever method is followed in deciding upon a timber operator, the owner will want to assure himself that the logger is financially responsible, that he is adequately covered by workmen's compensation insurance, that he has a reputation for honesty and fair dealing, and that he also has a reputation for careful and workman-like performance on the job.

Marking Trees for Cutting

The general principles discussed earlier for handling timber stands for optimum yield should be followed when marking trees for sale. But other factors must be considered also. Primary among these are the requirements of the timber operator and of the market.

The timber operator or logging contractor has found by experience that he can "go broke" very easily on jobs that do not meet certain minimum necessities of size and operability. Costs of developing access roadways, loading areas, skid roads, and of bringing in heavy equipment must be spread out over sufficient volume to keep unit costs within bounds. Also, average volume per acre must be sufficient (usually at least 1,500 to 2,000 board feet) to justify moving onto a given part of the tract, especially where merchantable volume is light and scattered. Rough terrain means heavier operating costs and more damage to equipment and necessitates the harvest of larger total and per acre volumes to meet these costs. The logging contractor is in the business to make a profit above total costs, hence a prospective timber sale must be large enough to be attractive to him. This usually means a minimum of some 30,000 to 40,000 board feet. Smaller sales can be made, but for smaller sales the owner usually must expect to receive a lower price and to have less choice among operators. Also, the logger will be more insistent on taking all merchantable timber in one cut if the operation is marginal in size. Timber sales of 100,000 board feet or more are usually sufficient in size to attract reliable loggers in the eastern United States, though for top prices and competitive bidding up to one million feet may be necessary. Sales in the West must usually be considerably larger in volume.

The owner should recognize that many marked trees may be marginal or submarginal from the logger's standpoint, and he should reach a decision concerning which trees he shall require to be cut and which he will permit to be left standing at the discretion of the logger. Allowing some discretion is particularly important when there are beech and other trees susceptible to heartrot. The skilled logger can usually determine by tapping on such a marginal tree with an ax whether it is sound or defective. He, more even than the forester, is widely experienced in cutting trees with major and minor defects. Consequently, his judgment and opinion merit some respect. If the owner is in the woods with such a logger, he may agree to have questionable trees felled, the felling to be at his expense if they prove to be complete culls. The advent of rapid-cutting power chain saws has made the logger much more willing to cut trees of questionable value than when he had to do it with a hand-pulled crosscut saw. If the owner or his agent inspects the sale area frequently, they may be able to spot trees that have been overlooked or rejected by the logger, and the owner can examine such trees with the logger to decide what action is to be taken. It should be realized, too, that the logger is naturally biased against cutting any trees of low quality or low-value species, even though they may be sound and merchantable.

The first sale on a purchased tract is likely to yield but modest stumpage revenues because the owner will want to concentrate his timber marking on the residual trees left from earlier cuttings. Residual trees may be coarse branched or show evidence of decay and other defects, or they may be of less desirable species. An effort should be made to market as many of these as possible so as to free the land for more valuable individuals and species. If trees of small to medium size suitable for crop trees exist, these should be favored in marking operations. In young stands, crop trees are usually slightly smaller than the largest trees. These large ones can be removed first since they are more attractive to the logger and most repressive to the ultimate crop trees.

Fluctuations in timber markets from time to time make these lower-value sale chances either more or less attractive. Stumpage that cannot be sold one year may be moved readily another year. Where an owner has a timber tract of marginal or poor quality, he should, rather than sell on a logger's choice basis, examine the quality of material moving into nearby mills and determine whether the timing is favorable for offering his timber within the existing market. If not, he could serve himself and his forest much better by waiting until the market becomes more favorable.

Contract of Sale

A written contract of sale protects both the owner and the timber operator. The owner sets forth exactly what he expects of the operator and the operator, in turn, of the owner. The timber sale contract should specify the location of the sale and boundaries of the area to be covered. It should specify that the owner is, in fact, the owner of the property and that he agrees to protect the logger against any claims that may be made upon him because of a faulty title or disputed boundaries. The contract indicates the amount of timber to be offered, in general terms, and the species available for cutting. It specifies the price to be paid by the timber operator, either as a lump sum or at so much per thousand board feet, by species, for saw logs and per cord for pulpwood. It specifies the log rule to be used in the case of sawtimber, and the length of the bolts in the case of pulpwood or other products. Minimum specifications for a merchantable log and for utilization standards in the woods are spelled out. It provides for an advanced payment or deposit and for a performance bond to assure that the logger will perform the contract that he has signed. It specifies whether the owner or his agent will scale the logs, or it may contain a clause in which the owner agrees to accept the scale offered the logger at the mill. If the latter is the case, the owner should reserve the right to specify the mill to which all logs are to be delivered.

The owner, in this case, may make an arrangement with the log buyer or the mill to send him the scale of all logs delivered from his property. This leaves the owner unprotected against possible collusion between the logger and the mill buyer. Also, it is possible that the logger may make delivery to two or more buyers, in which case it would be possible for him to remove some material without paying for it. Most mill operators are, however, meticulous in making sure that the logs they receive are paid for, and they generally cooperate with the owner.

Acting in this manner they avoid unpleasant and sometimes costly claims or lawsuits.

The sale contract may also provide for a penalty for deliberately cutting unmarked trees, though this penalty would usually be waived in the case of trees unavoidably or accidentally damaged in logging sufficient to require cutting. The owner should recognize, of course, that it is relatively easy for a logger to damage deliberately a high-quality unmarked tree on which he could make a profit.

The contract should specify that operations may not begin until the logger's insurance company has furnished the owner a statement that workmen's compensation insurance is carried by the logger and that the owner will be notified by the company if the insurance is cancelled for any reason. Workmen's compensation statutes in most states were enacted under the influence of labor unions, and they tend to place the full burden on the employer. If the logger is strictly an independent contractor working with a partner or relative, he may not be obliged to carry insurance (see Chapter III). Many operators are of this type. Since insurance for logging in some states is quite expensive, the small operator may try to avoid carrying it. A mere contract of sale is not necessarily sufficient to exempt the forest owner from liability for accident on his property, even though the logger was fully at fault. Also, the owner has no way of determining whether any such accident occurred on his property or elsewhere. Any supervision of operations by the owner tends to implicate him as an employer. Proof that the logger is carrying valid compensation insurance is the landowner's only real protection.

The contract will specify what usage, if any, may be made of the owner's roads and where and to what standard new logging roads may be constructed, or provide that their location may be mutually agreed upon. It will specify certain things with reference to the method of logging, that is, whether tree-length skidding is to be permitted, what type of skidding tractors may be used, and what penalties, if any, are to be invoked for damage to trees as a result of felling and skidding operations. Even the most skillful logger is bound to cause some damage when he fells a large tree. Since logging damage and opinion about whether a tree is merchantable are two issues that are likely to lead to disagreement, the contract should specify how disputes are to be settled if they cannot be handled directly by the owner, his agent, and the logger.

The time and method of payment for trees cut should also be carefully set forth in the contract. Usually advance payments are kept at a level sufficient to cover the value of any trees that are felled. A statement is usually included to make the sale binding on executors and heirs in the event of death of the owner. The contract should also specify means of terminating it, should either the owner or the logger default on his part of the contract. Other provisions that may be written into the contract include the maintenance of roads used by the logger, stump height, lopping of tops, removal of large trees, repairing of fences and trails, control of operations by the logger, and the duration of the contract. Since a contract of sale is somewhat complicated, the owner would be wise to have the services of a consulting forester in drawing up the contract and then have the resulting document reviewed by a lawyer for legal form. An attorney is not necessarily qualified to draw a logging contract without the advice of a forester. Sample contracts may be available in the state district forester's office.

One further point should be mentioned. The cooperation of the logger can be more readily obtained if the contract of sale and specifications therein are familiar to him. Insistence by the owner on unfamiliar log rules, elaborate provisions on logging methods, and other details may be self-defeating. It is better to have the willing cooperation of the logger than an air-tight contract full of penalty provisions. For this reason, contracts in local use, if well drawn, are to be preferred, with modifications to meet the particular needs of the case.

Supervising the Sale

Where possible, the owner or his agent should visit the operation at least once a week while active logging operations are under way. He should search the area for evidence of unmarked trees being cut, for high stumps, excessive "long-butting" of trees having internal defects, undue damage to standing trees as a result of felling and skidding, conformance to state laws with respect to top-lopping, for location of roads, and damage, if any, to existing roads, for general quality of workmanship, for any marked trees that have not been cut that are not obviously culls, and trees lodged during felling and not brought to the ground. He should make his presence known to the logger when he visits the cutting operations so that they may discuss any questions either may have. It is important that any infraction of the contract be called to the logger's attention promptly, since failing to do so may allow a precedent to become established and lead to serious misunderstanding later on. All in all, it is better to warn the logger promptly of any infraction and get the issue settled promptly. It is well to try to establish friendly relations with the logger so that he will be inclined to cooperate, rather than seek ways to cut corners at the expense of the owner.

If the owner is dependent upon mill buyers to scale his products, he should visit them and discuss with them his operation and performance of his loggers. The goodwill of buyers is also worth a great deal to the forest owner. Also, they generally know what is going on in the neighborhood and are in a position to assess the logger's reliability. Having a local custodian to check on the operations when the owner is unable to do so is also a good way to insure compliance with the contract and to be sure that proper payment is made. If the custodian is commissioned by a small percentage of the proceeds from the timber sale, he will have an incentive for seeing to it that full payment is made by the logger for all timber removed.

Joint Timber Sales

When the forest owner has but a small volume of timber to be sold at one time, he may find it advantageous to join with his neighbors in offering timber from two or more nearby properties in a single sale, or series of separate sales. This makes the operation much more attractive to the logger and may result in securing both a more reliable operator and a higher price for the stumpage. Such joint sales can, in fact, be worked out on a long-term basis so that the owners continue to enjoy the advantages of large-sized as opposed to small-sized operations. If more than two or three owners are involved, it is well to work out separate contractual agreements; in fact, it may be best to do so in any case, though this contract may be only a clause in the sale contract. Joint operations are much more easily carried out if the owners can agree upon a single individual as agent. This agent can then deal directly with the logger and keep separate records for each ownership or each sale area. Another way to obtain some of the same advantages is to employ a consultant logging or forestry firm that specializes in making timber sales and, hence, has up-to-date information on prices, logging methods, and loggers. Such an individual may operate as an agent of the owner without the owner's being obliged directly to enter negotiations with neighboring forest owners.

Summary

Timber sales bring in income and can be used to improve both the health and quality of the forest growing stock. It is through selling timber that the owner can make his impress on the forest, and only through making sales may all the efforts of the owner be converted into revenue.

Information on markets for timber can be had from local foresters, sawmill operators, and other timber buyers.

Sales may be made on a lump-sum, diameter-limit, land-clearing, or marked-tree basis. The last is generally most satisfactory to the property owner. Marked trees may be sold on the basis of standing tree volume (tree measurement sale), or by log scale.

Logs are bought and sold on their scale by a log rule. The log rule to be used should be specified in the contract of sale.

Selecting a reliable logger is important, and references should be sought from mill log buyers, foresters, and other landowners.

Marking trees for cutting is a job for a skilled forester; only after the owner gains experience should he undertake the task.

A written contract of sale should be drawn up to protect both landowner and logger. A forester's help is needed in this.

Timber sales should be inspected periodically for conformance to contract, and any nonconformance should be brought promptly to the logger's attention.

Owners having less than 50,000 board feet to offer for sale at one time might consider joining with their neighbors to make a joint sale that would be more attractive to loggers and likely to bring a better price.

LITERATURE CITED

1. Reginald D. Forbes and Arthur B. Meyer, eds., *Forestry Handbook* (New York: Ronald Press, 1955), Sec. 1, pp. 53-59.

 **VII**

Increasing Forest Productivity

The forest owner needs to have in mind certain basic concepts to guide him in his efforts to improve the productivity of his property. These are:

1) fixed costs as opposed to variable costs,
2) potential versus feasible land productivity,
3) responsiveness of lands and forests to cultural treatments,
4) variable returns per unit expenditure for cultural treatments,
5) alternate use of unresponsive lands.

Fixed Versus Variable Costs

In common with other entrepreneurs, the forest owner must meet both fixed and variable costs. Land taxes, interest, custodial fees, other protection costs, and maintenance of roads, structures, and boundaries are examples of costs that must be met just to hold the property and prevent deterioration. They may be considered to be fixed, or overhead, costs. Such costs, in themselves, add nothing to the natural productivity of the property, except to maintain it while timber grows. Expenditures for tree planting, cultural care of plantations, thinning, improvement cuttings, harvest cuttings, and reproduction of the forest all increase the productivity or bring in income directly. These costs vary with the level of productive activity, and need not be incurred unless productive use is desired. As a general principle, a manager will seek to keep his fixed costs low in proportion to variable or production costs, but this

151

may not be a wise expedient in the case of a forest property. In reality, the above concept of two categories of costs does not apply strictly to a forestry business. The forest, itself, really corresponds to a factory and the standing trees in it to the machinery for production. The trees are at the same time the product of the factory. Furthermore, the productive machines operate continuously producing good and bad products at a rate determined mainly by the forest factory and the extent to which the factory space is fully utilized by productive machines. The owner, once he has acquired the factory, can do little to improve its basic productivity except to install additional machines in unoccupied space. He can do a great deal in terms of quality control of product by replacing antiquated machinery which occupies much space but produces only inferior or useless products and by removing machines of poor design to provide more space for those well designed for efficient use of space. Here sentiment enters, because the antiquated, limby, hollow-trunked oak tree may provide a den for a family of raccoons and acorns for deer and squirrels. Also, it may have a spreading crown of pleasing shape. If it is valued for these features, it may be kept and charged to the personal pleasure it affords. The point to keep in mind here is that only a limited number of den trees will be occupied per acre. Most cut-over forests have quite a number of such trees.

This concept of the forest as a factory and the standing trees as machines manufacturing wood of varying quality is a useful one to keep in mind in the discussion that follows. With this understanding, the use of the terms "fixed" and "variable" costs has its value. Fixed costs, in relation to variable costs, can be lowered by acquiring compact forest holdings (generally, this is not easy to do), by increasing the volume of wood produced per acre, and by improving the quality of the products available for harvest.

There is also a certain efficiency to an intensive, as opposed to extensive, operation. The costs of land taxes, roads, boundary maintenance, and general protection tend to increase directly with the size, or perimeter, of the area. Forest growth may vary from a low of 100 board feet or even less up to 800 board feet or more per acre per year, and the owner is generally better off to have 1,000 acres yielding 800 board feet per acre per year rather than 8,000 acres yielding 100 board feet per acre per year.

Intensive forestry tends to pay off in other ways. By removing the less vigorous trees, the forest, generally, becomes more resistant to disease and other natural depredations. By frequent cuttings, trees that otherwise might die are used together with those less desirable trees that may be hampering the growth of better species. Thereby the owner sends to market all the wood that his forest produces.

The task faced by the forest owner, however, is considerably more complex than that of concentrating expenditures upon activities that yield maximum growth increases. The most expensive item is likely to be labor, and this factor is one which must be used with great skill and efficiency if it is to yield returns that exceed costs. The owner may well find it more profitable to acquire additional land, especially if it is well stocked with growing timber, than to incur the labor costs involved in planting or in rehabilitating an area covered mostly with cull trees or inferior species. The real concern is with total costs in relation to income and capital accumulation through growth.

Potential Versus Feasible Productivity

The growth capacity (productivity) of an area of forest land can be increased by a number of expedients. These include maintaining appropriate stocking with rapidly growing trees, removing trees by thinning or partial harvest when growth decline sets in, and possibly, in extreme cases, adding fertilizers or irrigating. A maximum point is eventually reached beyond which no additional stocking, cultural treatment, fertilizer, or water will give a response. This is conditioned by the efficiency of the photosynthetic process in green foliage for manufacturing wood cellulose and lignin by use of solar energy. No amount of effort by man can push the level of efficiency above its natural limit. Feasible land productivity, or that for which it is practical to strive, is much below this maximum. Water supply, mineral supply, temperature, and other site factors establish the level of growth capacity which is feasible. Costs of attaining productivity of wood volume above this level will exceed the value of the increased growth.

The owner must, therefore, accept the feasible productivity of his land as the goal which conditions the intensity of his management efforts. But he is not limited to this. He can divert this growth onto those trees that will yield him the highest financial return. This is one of the aims of forest managers. It is accomplished by favoring the most valuable species, by selecting individual trees that are rapidly growing and have well-formed boles and crowns, by keeping optimum stocking or stand density, and by reproducing a stand promptly after making a harvest cutting. Rarely will the average forest owner find it feasible to attempt irrigation or even general applications of fertilizers. A land area that is ill-suited for commercial timber growing had best be sold or left in the wild state for recreational or wildlife values, rather than intensively managed for timber production.

Responsiveness to Cultural Treatment

Feasible productivity is limited by the responsiveness of soil and forest stands to cultural treatment (manipulation of growing conditions). Little can be achieved in terms of added volume growth by any cultural treatment of stands growing on poor soil. Similarly, poor stands respond with less net gain from a given investment in treatment than do those with good composition. There is rarely little prospect of getting a significant increase in value by any treatments applied to such low-value, short-lived tree stands as gray birch, sassafras, and persimmon or even balsam fir, aspen, pitch pine, jack pine, or Virginia pine, especially if the trees are near their rotation age.

The prospective forest owner has already been cautioned against purchasing lands near natural tree limits in semi-arid regions, the far North, and on mountain slopes. He has also been warned against purchasing lands stocked primarily with species having little or no current or prospective market value. But, however discriminating he may have been in his purchases, some of his soils will produce more rapid growth than others, and some of his stands will contain better species and be more responsive to treatment than others. He will want to give priority in treatment to those that will produce the highest value response in relation to the costs involved. He will need the help of a forester in selecting the most responsive areas to favor.

Variability of Return on Production Investments

Just as soils and stands vary in their response to treatments, so do cultural operations vary in the financial return they will yield on necessary costs incurred. Fedkiw, Hopkins, and Stout[1] studied the economic expectations from pruning white pine in the Adirondack area. They found that trees properly selected, thinned, growing on a good site, and held for sufficient time to produce three diameter inches of clear material after the knots had been overgrown could be expected to return the pruning investment, plus up to 10.8 per cent interest compounded annually. With less favorable conditions, the earned interest rate was lower.

Studies by Stoltenberg, Marty, and Webster[2] showed that the returns to be expected in Pennsylvania forests varied widely with the type of operation performed, the site quality, and the composition of the timber stand on which the job was done. For example, thinning a northern hardwood pole stand containing high-value species could be expected to yield

$12.00 to $16.00 per dollar of cost incurred in the thinning. Planting desirable species among scrub oak stands on a poor-quality site yielded, by contrast, but $0.15 per dollar of cost. The spread in returns is enormous, from one- to one hundred-fold. Other operations were distributed between the two extremes.

The relative returns from various forestry operations have only recently been subjected to economic analysis and, so far, but for a few specific cases. The owner would be wise to discuss this question with his consulting forester before deciding on which cultural measures he will undertake first on his property. Practices likely to yield a high return on the investment made are pruning top-quality sapling and pole hardwoods of choice species, killing over-topping cull trees, thinning or weeding stands of pole size, and pruning selected white pine. Practices yielding low returns on investment are conversion of brush lands to forest and any operations carried out on low-quality forest soil, on slow-growing trees, or where heavy costs of labor or machinery are incurred.

The owner should realize that these are but general guides. The actual returns which he can expect depend upon his specific property, his costs, the efficiency with which his operation is carried out, and his alternate rate of interest, that is, the interest he is paying or would be foregoing if he made the investment in timber growing. His income tax status, as mentioned earlier, also affects his overall return. Determining the return with precision requires accurate cost and returns data and involves compound interest calculations over a number of years into the future. Details of the methods used are given in textbooks on forest management and economics (see Annotated Bibliography).

Alternate Uses for Low Productive Lands

The reader at this point may be perplexed. The land he has acquired, or is about to acquire, has on it swampy areas, rocky

At rotation age the forest must be reproduced. In this case the advice of a
forester is needed to determine the most economical method for perpetuating
pine.

ridges and shallow soil, or areas of sand or hardpan soil with meager productivity. What is he to do with them? Such resistant sites are found on almost all sizable forest properties. The owner should follow one of two courses—ignore these areas in his plan of operation, or seek to use them for their most feasible purposes other than commercial timber growing. This returns him to the array of objectives defined for ownership at the outset. Rocky ridges may be used for interesting hiking trails; cliffs often afford an inspiring view. A small swamp may sometimes be converted to a pond at modest expense. Swamps are invariably attractive to wildlife that can bring the owner's family much pleasure. Swamps also may support specimens of lady slipper, cardinal flower, pitcher plant, sun dew, and other unusual plants that may be of interest. A sandy or hardpan soil too poor to grow timber may be well suited for producing Christmas trees. Forest openings and overlooks are attractive places for picnic spots, overnight lean-tos, and other recreational use. The owner will be wise to seek uses for them that yield satisfactions other than dollar income. One of the objectives of ownership is to make the forest attractive esthetically as well as financially profitable.

Programming Forest Improvement

The estate owner is almost certain to find that his property offers a wide variety of opportunities to carry out improvements that will increase the earning capacity of his forest. Where the owner utilizes the services of a consultant forester, the consultant and owner should go over the lands together, by compartments, to discuss various types of cultural attention that should be considered area by area. Estimates of priorities of importance and of the time and cost for each operation could be listed, so that the owner may better understand their impact upon his planning. The owner who desires to participate, personally, in carrying out certain operations and practices, can obtain specific instructions or demonstrations from his forester and later have his own work checked for suitability. For some operations the owner should arrange for direct guidance or supervision by the consultant forester, or for their being carried out under contract.

Forest improvement needs thus listed by the owner under guidance can be summarized for the forest as a whole. The estimated increase in dollar value over a given future time period that would result from each type of operation also should be worked out as closely as possible, and listed. The owner is then in a position to calculate relative rates of return or to decide priorities of jobs to schedule first, and how many he can afford to undertake. Usually he will discover that the work needed will require far more time than he can afford. He may also discover that the costs will exceed what he deems it prudent to invest. He must then weigh the cost to him of postponing or neglecting to carry out a particular improvement operation against that of borrowing funds to do it.

A description of the various operations normally desirable to enhance financial returns from a forest property follow.

Improvement Cuttings

In the average second-growth forest, much of the growth will be occurring on trees considered unmerchantable by the last logger who cut over the area. A logged-over timber lot in the eastern United States is apt to contain defective beech or oak trees, unwanted elm, hickory or hop-hornbeam; badly weeviled and, hence, coarse, limby white pines; clump growth of hardwoods where high quality is not likely; trees that have been split by wind or lightning; and those having decay in the trunks. As timber becomes scarce in a region, merchantability standards tend to be lowered to bring more wood on the market. Often it is possible to market a limited number of low-value trees, provided the logger is at the same time offered a reasonable number of good trees that he can harvest at a profit. Also, markets are gradually accepting more formerly undesirable tree species. Cutting that concentrates on removing the low-value species and trees to favor the better trees is an improvement cutting. Often it is combined with a thinning in the polewood and small-sized sawtimber.

Where improvement cutting is determined to be justifiable, it should be carried out as promptly as possible after acquiring a property in order to divert the growth potential to the young and thrifty trees of good species and form. There will inevitably be some undesirable trees remaining that the logger refuses to cut or will cut only if paid specifically to do so. These can be removed from competition with other trees by girdling (removing a band of bark around the stem) or by the use of a chemical silvicide (tree poison). A combination of girdling and use of a silvicide is preferable since the combined operation results in prompt killing and prevents the growing over that often follows girdling alone. A silvicide that is effective and safe for general use is 2,4,5-T, obtainable in farmers' supply stores. The tree killer can be applied by an oil can in a frill made with ax cuts around the stem. Deadening competitive cull trees is a relatively cheap and effective way of promoting the growth and improving the composition of the residual young stand. Without such an operation, the natural productivity in many forest stands will accrue mostly on unmerchantable trees with little useful growth being realized.

If the stand is well stocked with good younger trees, removing over-topping cull trees is one of the most productive forest investments. A workman can cover up to fifteen acres a day, depending upon the size and number of trees to be treated. If his work results in increasing the growth of merchantable trees by but twenty board feet per acre per year, the operation is likely to prove profitable.

Planting

Planting open areas to forest trees often has many advantages. It results in immediate stocking of the area so that it is no longer idle. Plantations, especially of conifers in a forest setting otherwise of hardwoods, are often esthetically pleasing. Planting makes possible the introduction of new species or strains into the forest stand, but this should be attempted only on sound advice. Forest geneticists have produced certain rapidly growing hybrids that may, in special circumstances, be feasible to plant on the forest property. A plantation can provide useful cover and food for wildlife. Highly valuable trees such as black walnut, yellow poplar, black cherry, and sugar maple may be introduced. Conifers have the advantage that Christmas trees may furnish a profitable early crop. Aid for planting as a conservation measure may be available to the owner through the Agricultural Conservation Program of the federal government and through various state programs.

Planting also has several disadvantages. Generally, it is costly. Even if the planting stock is available from the state at cost or less, the total expense of trees planted in the ground is likely to exceed twenty-five dollars an acre. Early returns, except from Christmas trees, are impossible. Plantations tend to be more susceptible than natural stands to diseases, insect attack, weather extremes, and physiological disturbances owing to improper soil conditions. Plantations require care to prevent the young trees from being over-topped and crowded by competing natural growth. This is another way of saying that much of the land that might be planted will reforest naturally, which may be both a cheaper and an altogether more satisfactory way of bringing in forest cover on open areas. Finally, the species planted may not have a good market when the trees mature.

However, when all advantages and disadvantages are weighed, one thing stands out: An owner has a keen personal interest in trees that he, himself, has planted. There is much satisfaction in watching them grow, and if he can harvest his own Christmas trees and a few for his neighbors, his satisfactions may justify the effort for a nominal acreage.

Planting should not be embarked upon without taking a careful look ahead and then obtaining specific advice from a competent forester experienced in providing tree planting service. Publicly employed foresters also will provide some guidance at nominal or no direct charge, and are a source of information on possible public financial aids. Machine planting is less costly than hand planting and often results in a better job. An owner having a considerable area to be planted should not plant it all in one year. Possible public aid is limited and planting mistakes are best corrected on small rather than large areas. Conifer plantations of different ages present an interesting appearance and provide Christmas trees over a long period of time. Wildlife cover is also provided for a long time in such forests.

The easier planting terrain and better sites should be selected first so that experience may be gained with less likelihood of failure. Planting presents little difficulty on level, sandy soils where planting machines can be used. Here competing vegetation may be removed by furrowing. Rich loam soils are more productive than sandy soils, but these are usually kept in agricultural production. Hay crops or pasturage may yield an income better than that to be expected from planting trees. However, such lands are the ones that also will yield the highest returns if planted. They are better suited to, and should be reserved for, valuable hardwoods.

Most planting in the northeastern United States has been made with red pine. This conifer species is generally hardy, grows on a wide variety of soils, is only moderately susceptible to insect and disease damage, and produces a quick forest cover. It has the disadvantages that it is not favored for Christmas trees and the trees when grown to merchantable size have a lower value than white pine and most hardwoods. In the southern United States, slash pine and loblolly pine are widely used. Both grow rapidly and may be harvested for pulpwood and sawtimber. In the western states, Douglas fir and ponderosa pine have been widely used. There are many other species that may prove preferable under given conditions. Local advice on species to use is imperative since forest trees vary in their growth characteristics with local soil conditions and differences in climate, and ultimate market potential should always be considered.

Care of Plantations

Most forest plantations require some degree of care. Usually, this means protecting them from fire, insects, and competing vegetation. Protection from fire is usually provided by public agencies, but the risk is high enough to require prudent judgment concerning location, access, and local practice. Aggressive weeds and low shrubs may over-top young planted trees and slow their growth or even kill them. Such competition can be removed by mowing with a scythe or power mower, or by using various herbicides. If the latter are to be applied as a foliage spray, care must be taken not to kill the planted trees along with their competitors. Assistance from a qualified forester should be obtained. Once a plantation is above the competing vegetation it will require little attention until the time at which the first thinning should be made. Occasionally, insect depredations reach such proportions that spraying may be necessary to control them.

At least one thinning may be needed at age fifteen to twenty-five years, before the trees are of sufficient size to make this operation a commercial cutting. Since there is as yet no harvest value involved, a practical way is to remove every third row in the plantation with a bulldozer. This is less costly and also makes a pathway for logging vehicles for later selective commercial thinnings.

Care of Young Natural Stands

Young natural stands can benefit from the same type of care extended to plantations. Fire, for example, should be kept out of them. They also need protection from insects, which may require spraying, though this is something not to be undertaken without competent advice. Also, young natural stands are almost certain to need thinning and weeding. If the young stand is made up of pines growing at a density of one or more per square foot, it may become completely stagnant. It is very difficult to select the trees that should be removed in such thickets. Unless some thinning is made, however, such stands become subject to heavy snow damage because the stems are thin in relation to height. Oftentimes the only practical method of thinning is to run through the stand at intervals with a tractor or bulldozer, thereby making lanes along which the better trees can grow. In young hardwood stands, however, thinning should favor preferred species and trees with straight single stems.

Another method of carrying out noncommercial thinnings is through the use of silvicides. These may be applied in ax cuts or, in some cases, as foliage or basal sprays. Silvicides are often cheap to apply and more effective than severing the stems. A natural stand has one advantage over a plantation in that the trees tend to be irregular in size and, hence, establish their own order of dominance. The dominant trees, in time, will form a canopy that suppresses the others. It is generally better in young hardwood stands to permit such natural thinning to take place rather than to attempt to assist nature before the trees have attained a diameter sufficiently large to make them useful for fuel.

Young natural stands are likely to have among them many trees with such ill-formed stems that they will not produce merchantable timber. These may be rapidly growing elm, or even such valuable trees as ash or black cherry. Quite commonly they grow in tight clusters which are sprouts from earlier stumps, and these are less desirable than single trees. Old cull trees or early invaders of an open field which have become excessively limby and, hence, useless for timber production, and that are suppressing valuable trees, are known as "wolf" trees. Their removal is just as important as the removal of cull trees left after logging.

Thinning young stands, particularly hardwoods, is likely to be one of the better-paying forest investments. It is to be highly recommended but must be skillfully done.

Thinning Pole Stands

When the trees have reached a diameter of six to eight inches, a commercial thinning becomes possible. Trees of this size can be removed and used for pulpwood, fuel, posts, or small poles. At this age, the trees that are most promising to be carried through as crop trees may be selected. All subsequent thinning operations may be carried out to favor the crop trees. The necessary amount of competition should be left to insure tall, straight, clean boles. After the crop trees have attained a minimum of seventeen to eighteen feet of clear length, or at least have no live branches below this height, they may be thinned periodically so as to preserve live crown for 40 to 50 per cent of the total height. In eastern forests, thinning pole-sized trees should be delayed if there is a luxuriant growth of shrubs and herbs beneath the stand.

Crop trees need number no more than 100 per acre in the case of conifers and may be as few as fifty trees per acre in the case of hardwoods. The largest trees in the stand, which tend to have large limbs, generally produce lower-quality lumber. The co-dominant trees, or dominant trees with small limbs, are good choices for crop trees. At each commercial thinning, any large "rough" trees that are interfering with the crop trees are the ones to be removed, together with those of merchantable size that may be expected to die before the next thinning period.

The severity of thinning will depend on its frequency. It is best to thin lightly and frequently rather than heavily at long intervals, provided it is possible to do so commercially. Light thinnings provide room enough for trees to grow well without large, heavy limbs. As a rule of thumb, a thinning should be no more severe than will result in crown closure within a five-year period. This can be estimated in the case of pines by counting back five years of growth on the side branches and projecting forward a growth of at least this much for the ensuing five years. On the other hand, for a thinning to pay its way there must be enough volume harvested to justify the cost, and this may require cutting one-third to one-half of the trees in the stand.

Another way to decide upon the intensity of thinning is through the use of normal yield tables. These tables, prepared by foresters, give information on the basal area in fully stocked stands of various sizes and ages. By basal area foresters mean the cross sectional area of all the tree stems on an acre as computed from their diameters four and one-half feet from the ground. It is possible to remove at least one-fourth, and sometimes as much as one-third, of the basal area in a thinning without appreciable decrease in the total growth rate per acre over the five- to ten-year period following thinning.

When thinning a stand of mixed conifers and hardwoods, or pure hardwoods alone, the first thinning should remove those species that are undesirable for crop trees. Among species that should be removed in an early thinning, provided market conditions are favorable, are beech, red maple, elm, hemlock, balsam fir, jack pine, and red pine for the northern United States and the low-value hardwoods in the southern states.

Pruning

Pruning young crop trees for a distance of eighteen feet (one log) or even thirty-four feet (two logs) above the ground may prove to be a financially profitable operation, especially if the owner has a nearby market for veneer logs or is in a position to benefit from the high-quality sawlogs that will result from pruning. To appreciate the value of pruning, one needs to understand the difference in market prices for lumber of various grades. Quotations from the *Commercial Bulletin* of February 6, 1965, for one-inch-by-six-inch white pine of various grades, per thousand board feet, f.o.b. Boston, were as indicated in Table 11.

TABLE 11
QUOTATIONS FOR WHITE PINE LUMBER

Grade of Lumber	Quotation
D and better select	$225-240
Number 1 and 2 common	160-180
Number 3 common	105-120
Number 4 common	80-90
Number 5 common (industrial)	55-70

The prices shown in Table 11 are for seasoned and surfaced lumber. Since the cost of harvesting, milling, seasoning, surfacing, transporting, and selling must all be subtracted from the price received, it is clear that little margin, if any, exists for stumpage to the landowner for trees that will produce only low grades of lumber. The costs incurred for producing and selling the higher grades from which real profits can be realized all along the line are no higher than those for handling low-grade material. It is for these reasons that stumpage prices vary from as low as ten dollars per thousand board feet for low-quality pine, beech, and elm, if, in fact, the logger will cut it at all, to twenty dollars for good-quality pine and fifty dollars to seventy dollars for better ash, cherry, hard maple, birch, and white oak. Veneer quality logs of birch, cherry, and walnut may bring as high as $200 to $400 per thousand board feet. There is ample margin available to recompense the owner adequately for costs of pruning pole-sized crop trees so they will produce veneer quality logs, provided the owner sells such trees to a veneer log buyer rather than to a sawmill logger on a lump sum transaction.

Pruning can best be done from a short, stable ladder with a

large-tooth hand saw. Pole saws also may be used, particularly for heights above twelve feet. Pruning wounds should be no larger than one and one-half inches in diameter so they will heal over within a five-year period or less. It is preferable to prune trees before or soon after the branches have died since, otherwise, loose knot formation occurs in the log. Ordinarily, it is possible to prune young pine trees up to a height that includes the lower three whorls of live branches without causing a noticeable decrease in growth. If as much as one-half the live crown is removed in pruning, the growth rate will be reduced by as much as one-third for the ensuing five-year period. Pruning in dense stands should be accompanied by thinning to stimulate growth.

Thinning in Sawlog Stands

Thinning in sawlog stands has two purposes: to control the rate of growth, and to harvest all commercial material that is grown. Controlling the growth rate is an art that has become highly developed on some industrial forests in the United States and on estates in Europe. The aim is to maintain growth rate at a uniform optimum level with minimum capital carried as growing stock.

Extremely rapid growth in conifers tends to produce weak, brittle wood of relatively low value both for construction and veneer. Such growth results primarily from large-topped, open-grown trees. Rapid growth in heavy hardwoods such as maple, on the other hand, tends to produce a harder and generally more valuable wood than that grown slowly. Slow-growing ash and hickory have a high percentage of springwood to summerwood and, hence, are weak, brittle, and less well-suited for handle stock, skis, and other athletic equipment requiring high strength.

The forest owner, therefore, should seek to grow his timber at as high a rate as possible without impairing wood quality. Rapid growth is desirable for maple, ash, hickory, and basswood, and a moderate rate of growth is preferred for pine, yellow birch, cherry, oak, and walnut. Rapid growth means five or fewer rings per inch; moderate growth is six to ten rings per inch, slow growth more than ten rings per inch.

Quality timber, when the tree is of sufficient diameter, is recognized by the appearance of the tree bole. If the tree is straight and free of branches for as much as two log lengths, and if it displays no scars or other indicators of defects beneath the surface, the logs will have a ready market and will command a good price. The longer the tree has been grown free from knots, the greater the percentage of clear lumber it will produce and the higher realization value it has to the buyer. Trees that have been pruned for veneer log production continue to increase in value at a more rapid rate than they increase in volume. The owner may, therefore, wish to keep such trees for as long as their growth rate is earning an attractive return on his investment in them. Veneer-quality trees ordinarily must be at least eighteen inches in diameter, and sawlog quality at least fifteen inches. The value of growth that accrues requires this base to be meaningful. Obviously, the loss that is incurred if a high-value tree happens to be windthrown or meets with other disaster increases the older it becomes, and the owner must decide for himself how long he can afford to take such a risk. Thinning operations that may be carried out at five-year intervals in young stands would gradually be extended to ten or more years as the trees get larger in size.

Sooner or later the owner is faced with the question of how long he should continue to hold a stand before making his final harvest cut and starting a new crop. Here he may calculate the net earnings from the land and the rate of return on his investment in growing stock and decide for himself whether it is adequate. He may also wish to carry the forest as a growing asset to provide funds for such personal aims as educating his children or building a new home. Usually, however, he will be influenced more by the element of time upon his decisions than by other factors.

Harvest and Reproduction Cuttings

Ultimately a time arrives in the life of a forest stand when growth has slowed and losses due to natural depredations indicate the timber should be harvested and a new crop started. If a stand has been carried to rather large size, advanced growth of younger trees to form much of a new crop may have become established throughout the stand, particularly in openings in the forest. In this case it is desirable to remove the old stand in two cutting operations spread a few years apart so that the young growth has opportunity to adjust gradually to more open conditions after cutting. If young growth is not present, the older trees may still be removed by two or more cuttings spread several years apart, the first of which will open up the stand sufficiently to encourage seed production and seedling establishment but still retain necessary forest site conditions; the second will remove the remainder of the trees after regeneration has become established.

What often happens, especially in stands that have not been carefully managed, is that too heavy a cut is made at once so that shrubs and other worthless vegetation invade the old stand and prevent the establishment of a new crop of tree seedlings. This calls for drastic measures. Controlled burning, going over the ground with a disc harrow to expose mineral soil, or planting seedlings directly may be required. Oftentimes, it is preferable to use herbicides to kill the unwanted vegetation, and in extreme cases it may be necessary to use a bulldozer and heavy disc to eliminate the shrubs and brush and prepare the ground for a new crop. In any case, once the young trees have become well established, the remaining old trees should be removed, taking care that a minimum amount of damage to the new crop occurs during the logging operation. This completes the prolonged cycle of forest cropping over one generation, and the owner starts again with a seedling forest which must be tended, weeded, thinned, improved, and eventually harvested some fifty years or more in the future.

The above instructions imply that the new forest stand will be even-aged, that is, the trees will vary no more than twenty years in age. It also implies clear-cutting of all remaining trees at rotation age. To many people such a drastic cutting may appear to be forest destruction. It is, however, the method generally followed by skillful foresters in Scandinavia and Germany, and by both industrial foresters and the government forest managers on national forests in the United States. Attempts to manage forests in uneven-aged stands have not proved best, even for such shade-resistant trees as northern hardwoods, spruce, and fir.

If an owner has but a small forest area, he can restrict his clear-cutting to small patches some one hundred feet or more in diameter. As these areas become restocked they can be extended in size until the entire stand is reproduced.

Special Measures to Improve Growth

Under special circumstances, a landowner may desire to go beyond the above normal practices to improve growth or for other improvement in parts of his forest area. Among measures he might consider are swamp drainage, fertilizing, and irrigation. These are likely to be uneconomic when large areas of naturally productive forest land are available but occasionally they may be justifiable if other purposes than tree growth are also served. Swamp drainage is carried out on a rather extensive scale in Russia, Finland, and Scandinavia. Government subsidies are offered landowners in certain countries, or the government itself may carry out the work. Extensive swamp drainage in northern Minnesota has resulted in only moderate increases in tree growth, too little to justify the cost of the operation.

Forest soils in some parts of the United States may be low in one or more of the basic plant nutrient elements. A classical example is potash deficiency discovered on light sandy soil of the Pack Demonstration Forest at Warrensburg, New

York. Here, by the application of 300 to 400 pounds of potassium chloride per acre, the height growth in a red pine plantation increased from two inches annually to sixteen to twenty-four inches annually, thereby salvaging the plantation from complete failure. However, such fertilizing is too costly for regular use. In other sections of the country, trace elements—those required only in minute quantities—may be found to be deficient. These can be applied in small amounts and produce outstanding response. Copper, cobalt, and zinc are examples of such elements. Many forest areas are suboptimal in basic plant nutrients and, hence, will show a response in tree growth through the application of fertilizer. As a general rule, however, the cost of the fertilizers and of applying them is likely to be considerably more than the value of the growth response. The virtue in applying fertilizers is that in critical areas one application may serve the purpose for an entire rotation, because the trace elements used by the tree mostly are returned to the soil for reuse when the leaves fall.

Irrigation of Forest Lands

Irrigation of forest lands is quite uncommon. It is practiced, to a limited extent, in Pakistan and Spain. Various measures to conserve moisture are used in Italy, Greece, Turkey, and other countries. One irrigated forest in Pakistan is unusually productive. The owner, the national government, realizes an income not only from sawtimber but also from fuelwood, posts, poles, faggots, leaves, castor beans, grass that grows along the irrigation ditches, and even bee pasturage for the production of honey. Irrigation will not prove feasible in the United States, however, except where the owner has a tree nursery or has other special needs.

Working for Special Products

In addition to veneer-quality logs, there are other special woods that command premium prices in certain markets. Demand fluctuates widely, but an owner who has such items as birdseye maple, curly maple or birch, burls, oak of stave quality, walnut crotches, or other highly figured and specialty woods should investigate possible markets. In Japan the highest price goes for a *Cryptomeria* pole of special fluting that is used for an alcove post in a tearoom. The number of such specialty uses was greater in the past than at present, owing in part to the development of substitutes. Hop-hornbeam was sought for hammer handles, persimmon for golf club heads, dogwood for shuttle stock, hickory for wagon and buggy spokes, ash for fork handles. Even today, hickory for skis and maple for bowling pins and shoe lasts command a good price. Such markets can be profitable if an owner is located to take advantage of them. However, changes in public taste and substitute materials are steadily reducing these opportunities.

Esthetics

Emphasis here has been placed on economic returns, but most forest owners are looking for other returns as well. In overview, these may be uppermost in guiding their actions.

A well-managed forest of tall, clean-boled, straight trees has its own esthetic appeal, but large areas of unbroken forests, especially if of a single species of conifer, tend to be monotonous. Nor may such a forest provide the highest long-range yield. Open glades and transition margins in the forest have their charm. It is here that one is most likely to see interesting wildlife. A forest interspersed with hay meadows or grazing land, or even with hawthorn and wild apple, generally is more interesting than one covered uniformly with timber.

Most forest properties will contain some old trees that have been passed over in earlier logging operations because they have coarse branches or evidence of decay. Such trees, especially if standing on the edge of the property or along an old fence row in a meadow, may have a pleasing form, and they may also serve as den trees for desirable wildlife such as flying squirrels, raccoons, or wood ducks. The owner can well afford to keep some of these trees for the satisfaction they give him. A hillside pasture overgrown with hawthorn is valueless for timber, but in springtime when in flower, it makes a cheery landscape. In late summer and fall these hillsides attract birds, deer, and other wildlife that are a desirable product of the forest environment. The owner who seeks to make every acre economically productive may be sacrificing some of these valuable intangibles of land ownership. Moreover, in good time his flower-covered slope will be invaded by maple, ash, and other valuable trees, in any case. To destroy all such areas for conifer plantations is neither essential nor economically wise.

The estate owner will naturally give esthetics priority near his homestead. Spacious open areas backed by fine old trees make a beautiful setting for rural living. They also enhance sales value.

Forest esthetics is largely a personal matter for each owner to decide. Help can be had from a landscape architect around the home. But for the property as a whole the owner himself must decide what is to be improved and what is to be left for nature to modify.

Summary

A forest owner must meet fixed costs and variable costs, capital costs and operating costs.

Fixed costs are those such as land taxes, custodial fees, carrying charges, and maintenance that continue irrespective of the level of activity. Variable costs are those, such as intermediate and harvest cuttings, that increase with level of operation.

Capital costs are those entailed in land acquisition, such as land surveys, title searches and the like; and forest improvements such as plantations, road building, and others that increase the intrinsic value of the property. Operating costs are those incurred for property management other than capital costs.

The returns on an investment in forest improvement vary widely with the type of operation and the character of the timber stand in which it is performed. Some, such as thinning northern hardwood pole stands on good soils, may yield a handsome return. On the other hand, planting scrub oak lands to conifers is almost certain to yield negative returns. An owner, generally, will wish to invest first in those operations that offer the highest financial returns. A forester's help is needed to guide such investments.

Improvement cuttings that can be made on a commercial basis are recommended for early scheduling.

Planting is recommended for the southern pine region but is likely to prove an unprofitable expenditure in northern forests.

Care of young stands should be kept as low in cost as is consistent with doing an effective job.

Thinning pole stands, especially if pulpwood may be removed, is recommended as one of the most remunerative of forest investments. Pruning of trees on good soil, if combined with thinning, is likely also to yield favorable returns.

Thinning in sawtimber stands can be made on a commercial basis and is one of the best ways to improve the future stand while obtaining income to meet current operations.

Ultimately the final timber harvest must be made and a new stand started. This requires the utmost care and skill if best results are to follow.

Rarely does it pay to irrigate or fertilize timber crops. It is much less costly to acquire lands not needing such treatments.

The forest owner should not overlook esthetics; some of his most satisfying returns may come from the amenities of his property.

LITERATURE CITED

1. John Fedkiw, Frederick S. Hopkins, Jr., and Neil J. Stout, "Economic Aspects of Growing High Quality Pine Through Pruning," *The Northeastern Logger* (April, 1960), 16-19, 22, 23, 39.

2. Carl H. Stoltenberg, Robert J. Marty, and Henry H. Webster, "Appraising Forestry Investment Opportunities—The Role of the Investor, the Forestry Practitioner, and the Researcher," *Proceedings,* Society of American Foresters (Washington, D.C., 1960), 82-85.

VIII

The Forest Owner in the Local Community

A forest holding of five hundred acres or more is an imposing piece of property. And because any productive land estate has the potential of yielding goods and services for both the owner and society in general, its ownership carries a moral obligation to use it wisely and well. Ownership carries the further obligation to pass the land on to posterity in at least as productive condition as when it was acquired. Indicating one's recognition of these obligations through personal action and example is one of the first steps toward building goodwill among the people of any community. Unless the owner continues to recognize and meet such obligations, he will court local displeasure and invite lack of consideration for his interests. A landowner who displays an obvious concern for the welfare of the community in which his property lies may be expected to be treated with respect.

The owner of a large forest property, 5,000 acres or more, wields considerable influence upon the local economic structure whether he wills it or not. This consideration should be a sobering one, and such influence should be exercised with discretion and directed toward constructive ends. Accepting the obligation to act in the community's best interest tends to make a major owner become more thoughtful and responsible in his actions than he might otherwise be. Ownership of a large forest property tends, therefore, to increase the stature of an individual as he performs the duties of responsible management. Yielding to this gentle, subtle, pervasive influence has a

176

favorable stimulus on character that can be one of the reward-
ing returns from estate ownership. But to reap such a personal reward, the owner must give of himself to the community as well. Unless he understands the community and
knows the people, his actions, however well intended, are
likely to be wide of the mark, or at least misinterpreted.

Rural people are well acquainted with their neighbors and
develop close friendships. This may seem like a false statement to a new family that has recently moved into a rural
area, for the local residents may be reserved until they have
had reasonable time to study the personalities and attitudes
of the new arrivals. This period of restraint may vary from a
few months to a few years, depending on how the new family
adjusts to the local culture. The acceptance process can be
shortened by letting the residents make friends rather than
by seeking to force one's acceptance upon them.

Among rural people are individuals of dignity, intelligence,
and native ingenuity, though they may lack college education.
Few are inured to the fast pace of doing things. Deliberation
and conservative action is common among rural people. Still,
in their business dealings, they may prove to be as sharp as a
Park Avenue executive.

Rural Communities

At first glance, most rural communities seem to have no
definite systems of organization. To some extent this may be
true because authority often is diffused among various political, social, and economic organizations. The formal structure
usually consists of the school, church, town meeting, and perhaps the chamber of commerce or a chapter of the Grange.
Rural residents, therefore, are limited to fewer associations,
but strong ties are generally developed among neighbors.

Owing to the rough topography, mountainous areas usually
develop communities that are small and often semi-isolated in
the winter. Such communities have few organized groups and

can pose real adjustment problems to a person of urban background.

A person interested in the development of the community in which he plans to live should learn whether or not the village is incorporated. An incorporated town has the following privileges which are not available to an unincorporated town:

1) Authority to issue bonds and have a funded debt
2) Right to enact town statutes
3) Right to maintain a fire and a police department
4) Power to tax.

Unincorporated towns are often little more than limited service centers with perhaps a general store, gas station, post office, and sometimes a church. These small communities, with populations of less than five hundred inhabitants, rarely provide any type of factories for employment.

Local Services and Their Proximity

The number of services a community has to offer is directly affected by the size of the population. With the modern automobile and the hard-surfaced road network any small community can be easily reached from a city within an hour or two at the most. Because of the advancements in highway transportation, the smaller cross road hamlets are diminishing from the rural scene. In most cases the old "cracker barrel" type store has modernized, providing some of the variety and lower prices of urban supermarkets. However, there are still many general stores in operation, and they are often a good place in which to get acquainted.

A person who is new in a rural community, whether as a summer resident or a permanent resident, should make weekly purchases from the general store, even though prices may be somewhat higher than in a city market. Although one may save a few dollars in the aggregate by purchasing groceries weekly at a chain store in another community, this sum will never compensate for the neighborhood goodwill and acceptance that could have been established. Local storekeepers are valuable acquaintances; they know most everyone in the area and will be able, for example, to recommend reliable persons for work one may need to have done. They are also aware of the day-to-day happenings in the area and can be very helpful in a time of need if the forest owner is regarded as a real neighbor.

Owners planning year-round residence should investigate the adequacy and type of local schools. Interest displayed in schools also helps a new family to get acquainted and to become adjusted to the community. Frequently the forest owner's background and experience could prove to be an outstanding asset to local boards or educational programs. Children who have begun their education in urban schools may find the following differences in a rural school: fewer varsity sports and extracurricular activities, fewer elective courses, and smaller, less adequate libraries. Before parents take up residence in a rural area, the high school curriculum should be reviewed to note whether the necessary prerequisite courses for entrance to college are offered. In many states one may well find that the centralized or district school serving a wide rural area is quite comparable in scope and quality to those in urban areas. The academic rating of a high school can be obtained by writing to the state university or the state board of education or by checking with the school principal to find out how many of his students were admitted to college and obtained degrees.

Churches in rural communities have undergone change. The small churches scattered throughout the countryside have yielded to the rural community church, and the small congregations have merged into larger congregations. Rural community churches serve the social as well as the religious needs of the people. Scouting groups, women's service societies, and men's brotherhood groups are just a few of the organizations sponsored by the church. The rural church is the most active organization in the community, and it is often the only unifying force in a rural area. Its growth depends greatly on the economic activities of the community.

Crime in rural areas is less noticeable than in cities and is seldom organized. The decline of economic stability in rural areas has been the major cause for rural crime increase. Professor Lane W. Lancaster, in his book *Government in Rural America*,[1] points out that the rural crime problem is due to two groups. Least subject to local corrective action are the more or less frequent forages by experienced lawbreakers from outside the area. Indigenous delinquents are the second group. These may be dealt with, in part, by strengthening agencies in the community that provide indirect control through constructive recreational and other opportunities and that promote good citizenship. Appropriate social welfare may also help to discourage antisocial behavior. Probably the most serious crime problem an absentee owner would encounter is breaking and entry. A local custodian is a strong deterrent to misuse of both timberland and buildings.

The protection of rural areas is carried out by the county sheriff's office and the state police. Because their duties are more inclusive and their powers are less limited, the state police are the major factor in law enforcement.

Other local services that the new landowner should consider and evaluate in light of his needs are as follows:

1. Water supply

   a) What is the source and possibility of shortage during a dry period?

   b) How safe is the present supply? The source should always be at a higher elevation than any undesirable drainage. Where one is a summer resident, he should have the water analyzed each year.

   c) If one's rural residence is not too far out of town, there is the possibility of extending the closest town water line, but this is usually rather expensive.

2. Mail

   The postmaster in the closest post office will be glad to advise whether a given location is on a rural delivery route or whether one must pick up mail from the post office.

3. Telephone

   Telephone service for an absentee owner, unless readily

accessible, may be too costly for the benefit derived. The usual practice is to use the village pay phone, or the neighbors' for any emergency calls.

4. Doctors and medical care

Rural doctors are usually general practitioners and serve the people at all hours and in all types of weather. They cover vast areas, and their time is limited. One should know how to reach a doctor in time of need and should be acquainted with the closest hospital. A practice worth immediate attention is that of maintaining a well-equipped first-aid kit and learning how to use it. The American Red Cross publishes an up-to-date first-aid manual which includes a check list for preparing your own first-aid kit.

5. Fire department

Rural fire departments are volunteer organizations, usually well equipped and trained in the essentials of fire suppression. When the fire alarm is sounded, all volunteers respond readily and perform their assigned jobs at the site of the fire. They provide efficient protection against grass fires as well as forest fires, and are usually tied into both the fire-detection and the mutual-aid systems. Fire fighting in rural areas is one of the greatest cooperative efforts. A ready source of water supply for emergency fire-fighting equipment is desirable; in less accessible areas a portable fire pump may save the day.

6. Roads and transportation

Town and county roads are maintained and plowed of snow during the winter. This service is not extended to private roads; therefore, the cost of maintaining a private road is always a factor to consider before purchasing a home far removed from the public road. A few towns in rural areas are fortunate to be on a bus route, but in most cases the automobile is the main means of transportation.

7. Local newspaper and radio station

Rural towns do not generally have the population to maintain their own town paper or radio station. Instead, the towns frequently cooperate in forming a regional paper and radio station. Each town has a few columns in the paper for the reporting of the local news. The regional newspapers are usually published weekly, serving as a community coordinator as well as a link between the towns that the paper serves.

8. Local organizations

Depending on their interests, the owner or his family may be interested in joining one or more of the following organizations:

a) Farmer cooperative, just one of many farmer-oriented organizations

b) Fish and game club

c) Water conservation association

d) 4-H Club

e) Boy Scouts

f) Parent-Teacher Association

g) Chamber of Commerce

h) Service clubs

i) Local fire department

9. Libraries

Libraries in rural areas are often poorly financed or even nonexistent. The latest trend in rural areas is circulating books by means of bookmobiles, or traveling libraries. These bookmobiles arrive in town on a specified day, lending books to those interested.

Local Governments

In rural areas the taxpayer comes in contact with the village or town, the township, the county, and the school district. There are also special districts such as highway, fire and soil conservation. Governmental organizations and services vary from state to state. It is well to become informed concerning the structure and operation of the several units. As a rural landowner, the forest property manager will need to have close contact with several county officials. The intimacy that exists between residents and government officers in rural areas

A comfortable home that fits into the forest environment may mean the difference between an estate that is a joy and one that is a burden.

is generally a new experience to the urban dweller. His opportunity to participate significantly in local governmental affairs is good and should not be shunned. A person purchasing land will come into contact with the following county officials by the time his transactions are complete: assessor, county clerk, collector of taxes, registrar of deeds, and often the surveyor or engineer.

As the forest owner establishes himself with his new community, meets officials, establishes relations with local stores, banks, schools, churches, physicians, and lawyers; and as he purchases land, improves it, makes timber sales, and deals with timber buyers, he may find that he has a new image— that of a rural gentleman. Depending on the time he can spend on his property, he may find himself gradually becoming a citizen of local importance. He may be called upon to serve in various community organizations and find himself sitting on boards of directors of local banks and businesses. Thus he can enjoy, during his productive years, some of the best of both leisurely rural and sophisticated urban living.

When retirement years approach, he may gradually spend more and more time on his forest estate. With advanced business or professional duties comes increased need for penetrating study, reflection, and policy formulation of the sort done better away from the pressure of telephone calls, visitors, conferences, and a crowded basket of mail. It becomes, therefore, easier to shift to the role of senior consultant and advisor when retirement comes.

Thereafter the forest holding offers a home, an interesting but not too-demanding business, and an important service to perform that can make retirement a quiet pleasure rather than a frustrating search for deferred satisfactions that require the energy of younger years.

Summary

Ownership of a sizable forest property carries with it obligations to manage the holding in such a manner as to meet public needs as well as satisfy private desires. By meeting his obligations, the owner may become a man of stature and influence in the local community. Acceptance of this role with dignity and grace can be one of the pleasures of ownership. For these and other reasons he should seek to understand the local governmental structure and its functioning, as well as the services it provides.

If the owner spends much time on his property—and he can scarcely reap the rewards of ownership without doing so—he must identify himself with the community and seek to serve it as it, in turn, serves him. Ample opportunities to perform such service exist in almost all communities. The acquaintances community service affords with those responsible for local government and other services will encourage fair treatment and readiness to help in cases of need.

In this way the forest holding develops as a second home, one to be enjoyed with increasing frequency as the years advance. With retirement from a more exacting employment, the forest estate may provide just that source of stimulus and adventure to make the years of leisure a time of satisfying creativity.

Literature Cited

1. Lane W. Lancaster, *Government in Rural America,* 2nd ed. (New York: Van Nostrand, 1952), 187.

Acquiring Understanding and Competence

Some of the deeper satisfaction that comes from owning and managing a forest property arises from the owner's acquiring competence and applying his knowledge to the improvement of his own forest land. Further, managing a forest holding, if it is of sufficient size to bring in an annual income, must be regarded at least as a serious hobby.

Acquiring a desirable level of understanding and competence takes some time. It is, perhaps, best done by integrating that which may be learned from books with that which personal observation and practice in the field contributes and makes interesting and challenging to the owner. Increased skills and assurance may be built up over a period of years. The owner will gradually depend more and more upon his own knowledge both of forests and forestry, and of his own specific woodland resources. In time, many individuals can develop sufficient knowledge of timber and basic instruments to reach reasonable judgments in their investments and operations, rather than relying largely on the services of consulting foresters. The forest owner would be well advised, however, to be sure of his facts and his understanding of them before making major investment decisions, or decisions on timber sales and other matters involving significant financial considerations.

This Appendix and the Annotated Bibliography that follows are designed to help the reader gain background knowledge, arrive at some modest practical understanding of forest management methods, and acquaint himself with some of the common practices and instruments useful to the interested forest landowner.

Forestry Tools and Instruments

The forest owner may wish to equip himself with some of the basic

187

tools for timber stand improvement and other nominal woods work on his property, or for conducting surveys and tree measurements to increase his own sense of awareness and competence in managing his timber assets. These tools and instruments can be obtained from forestry supply houses whose advertisements appear in the popular *American Forests* magazine and the professional *Journal of Forestry* and from various other sources. Agricultural suppliers may have some of them locally. There are numerous instruments and items of equipment that would prove useful, depending upon the extent of operating activity contemplated. The tools listed below are considered basic.

TOOLS FOR WOODS WORK

1) *Axes.* A reasonably heavy ax is needed for the chopping work that occasionally arises, especially when fireplace wood is used and the owner removes his lower-grade trees for this purpose. A small hand ax is also a desirable tool for carrying while making inspection trips in the woods. Some people use the war-surplus machete for cutting brush along survey lines and around young planted trees. Hand cutting tools are very useful but they can also be very dangerous in unpracticed hands. These blade tools are effective where timber-stand improvement work with use of tree poisons is undertaken, and other tools have been developed specifically for such use.

2) *Hand saws.* A coarse-toothed crosscut saw, suitable for felling smaller trees and cutting them up, is usually a necessity. Some woodsmen prefer the Swedish-style steel bucksaw. Any major sawing work in felling or bucking trees should be done with a power saw. Where light pruning of better quality young conifer or hardwood trees is contemplated, one of the best tools is the twenty-two-inch Bushman hand saw with very coarse 3/8-inch crosscut teeth. For work above six feet, a good-quality pole pruning saw is easy to use and is efficient to about sixteen or seventeen feet.

3) *Power saw.* The lightweight gasoline-powered chain saw, now reliable and efficient, has become an amazing labor saver. A number of manufacturers produce power chain saws that are suitable for felling trees up to fifteen inches in diameter and are also efficient for cutting fuelwood and performing other relatively light duty around a forest estate. If the owner likes to do such work himself, they are well worth the nominal investment. He should remember, though, that like all power tools they are dangerous in careless or inexperienced use.

4) *Peavey.* If the owner intends to fell any trees himself or have them felled by his immediate employees, a peavey for rolling logs is an important need.

5) *Paint gun.* The easiest way to designate trees to be cut for harvest, or for stand improvement or thinning, is with a hand-operated paint gun that squirts a fine stream of prepared tree paint. Paints of different but bright colors can be used similarly for boundary-line tree marking.

TOOLS FOR FORESTRY MEASUREMENT

1) *Compass.* The landowner will probably not do any land surveying as such, but nevertheless he will find certain surveying equipment highly useful in other ways, such as running inventory lines or rough boundaries, or locating woods, roads and trails. A good hand compass made in Finland is compact, accurate, quick in use, and quite adequate. It is available from forestry supply houses.

2) *Steel tape.* A two-chain (132 feet) steel surveyor's tape with topographic trailer is preferable, but the owner may wish to use a 100-foot surveyor's tape for the kind of measuring he has in mind.

3) *Angle measures.* An instrument for handily measuring vertical angles has many uses in the forest, such as determining tree and log heights and changes in land elevation. A topographic or per cent Abney level is commonly used, or a clinometer is satisfactory. Various newer instruments are also available from forestry supply houses.

4) *Traverse board.* The traverse board is relatively easy to use and has advantages where sketchy surveying and mapping may be desired by the estate owner. Much orientation measurement in forestry can be done satisfactorily by using a hand compass for direction and pacing for distance.

5) *Diameter measures.* It is very desirable to have one or more of the common instruments for measuring the diameters of trees. Calipers are simple and accurate but clumsy to handle. A diameter tape, compact to carry and easy to use, is preferred by most professional foresters.

6) *Growth measures.* A steel increment borer is a useful instrument for the landowner who takes a serious interest in determining growth rates. This small tool enables the user to extract a thin radial core of wood from a tree, which upon close examination of the annual growth rings reveals how much diameter growth the tree has been producing. In making increment borings one should slant the hole upward so that moisture will not accumulate and cause decay before the hole grows closed.

7) *Other instruments.* Other useful instruments that some forest owners may wish to obtain, depending on their activity, include a pocket stereoscope for use with aerial photographs, a modest set of drafting instruments including map board, and a small adding machine—there can be a surprising amount of data involved in keeping reliable forest records.

Associations and Affiliations

The experiences and interests of the forest owner that help build up his own understanding and competence in managing his property may be further supplemented and strengthened through association with other people having similar interests. Several types of associations are enumerated here. The individual owner may find occasion to become affiliated with one or more of these in his geographic region. The objectives, types of activity, nature of membership, services, and similar considerations for each such association should be explored carefully to determine which may come nearer to serving the individual's particular interests.

STATE FORESTRY AND CONSERVATION ORGANIZATIONS

There is a state forestry association in nearly every state where there is extensive forest area in private ownership. The characteristics of these associations are generally similar. Their programs include public education, promotion of conservation legislation, provision of a forum or active service for exchange of information on problems and new ideas, and occasional on-the-ground project assistance to satisfy a perceived need for some immediate action. They usually publish a magazine or newsletter, which is the primary means of communication with the membership. The membership is made up of voluntary dues-paying individuals of varying circumstances who are interested in forest resource matters. The general membership usually assumes little responsibility to the association or its program beyond payment of the annual dues of five or ten dollars.

These associations vary widely in their aims and programs. Some take strong interest in practical forestry and in enabling privately owned woodland to carry its own costs. Examples here are the Connecticut Forest and Park Association, Inc., the New York Forest Owners Association, and the Georgia Forestry Association. Others, such as the Vermont Timberland Owners Association or the California Forest Protective Association, give primary emphasis to fire protection. The preservation of an existing resource is the central theme of some of these associations, such as the Association for the Protection of the Adirondacks or the Save-the-Redwoods League. Many of them, however, aim at advancing the cause of good forestry, public and private, so that forest lands will be developed as fully as possible and used effectively for the benefit of all.

REGIONAL AND INDUSTRIAL ASSOCIATIONS

The forest owner is likely to find considerable mutuality of interest between his aims and those of certain regional associations or industrial groups in forestry. Depending upon his location, he may wish to take advantage of services or technical information available to participating members. Some of these associations have publications that can be obtained by those interested persons who are ineligible for membership. Several associations are noted here to help the forest owner reach a judgment on the type of affiliation and information that may be available to him.

1) New England Forestry Foundation, Boston, Massachusetts. This is a nonprofit corporation operating through forest management centers across New England to provide forestry service to woodland owners at cost.

2) Forest Farmers Association, Atlanta, Georgia. This organization of timberland owners speaks for the southern owner on all types of practical management problems. Its monthly publication, *Forest Farmer,* is labeled as the magazine of forestry in practice, and is an interesting and helpful guide to forest landowners wherever located.

3) Forest Industries Committee on Timber Valuation and Taxation, Washington, D.C. This industrially supported group periodically publishes the *Timber Tax Journal,* which provides much helpful information on current tax developments affecting forest land.

4) American Forest Products Industries, Inc., Washington, D.C. Membership is restricted to associations and companies. The AFPI develops and promotes sound, practicable forest operations and actively sponsors the nationwide programs known as Trees for Tomorrow, Keep America (or your state) Green, More Trees for (your state), and the registered Tree Farms system. It also distributes helpful literature.

NATIONAL ORGANIZATIONS

There are many nationwide organizations dealing with forestry development or natural resources conservation whose programs or publications might be of interest to the private forest owner. Relatively few of these would provide the specific practical information on local questions that the individual landowner frequently desires. They are, however, excellent national sounding boards on trends, legislation, and public reactions on matters that commonly have impact upon how the forest owner may react locally. Affiliation with these national groups is by no means necessary to estate ownership, but one or more of them may offer programs or publications of especial interest to the individual or to his family.

Several of the more pertinent groups and their publications are: American Forestry Association (*American Forests*), American Nature Association (*Nature Magazine*), National Audubon Society (*Audubon Magazine*), The National Grange (*National Grange Monthly*), and the Izaac Walton League (*Outdoor America*).

The Society of American Foresters is the organization to which professional foresters belong. Affiliation with local chapters, or sections, is possible to the layman. The Society publishes the *Journal of Forestry* and *Forest Science* as well as proceedings and various books and pamphlets of professional interest.

Selecting and Using Professional Help

The forest owner will need the services of a consulting forester, an attorney, an accountant and, from time to time, of a title examiner and surveyor. He may also use, at times, a land appraiser, timber broker, and real estate specialist. He will want to consult others—bankers, timber buyers, loggers, and perhaps an insurance underwriter.

THE CONSULTING FORESTER

The consulting forester is the key man for advice on the forest estate enterprise. It is he who understands the technology of a forest enterprise, can evaluate the land and timber and estimate future growth possibilities, and has best overall grasp of the business. A competent consulting forester can, in fact, under general guidance, take responsibility for both acquisition of the estate and its subsequent management. As with other professional men, his time is costly. Moreover, many of the services he performs are time consuming—estimating timber, projecting growth, making a timber sale, and purchasing a property.

The first task is to locate a competent and reliable man. Lists of consulting firms can be had from the Society of American Foresters in Washington, D.C., or from the state forester. Personal references also should be obtained. These can be had from the forester's banker, other local citizens who know of his work and reputation, and from his former clients. A visit to his office should be made to get acquainted and outline general plans and objectives. The consultant can then inform the prospective owner of the services he can provide, give an estimate of his fees, and outline what the owner can expect in the way of specific help. He can also tell the owner what he will need to know about the owner's objectives and resources.

At the second interview, the client should be prepared to tell the consultant forester of his personal situation—family, income, savings, what his objectives of ownership are and their relative importance and value to him, tell how much he is prepared to invest in the property and how long he is prepared to wait for a given level of financial return, where he wishes his forest land to be located and what improvements it should have. He should also reveal how much time he, personally, is prepared to devote to the project.

The consultant forester can almost immediately inform him as to whether or not his proposal is realizable and, if not, how it might be modified to make it so. If the client has already picked out a key property, the forester can go over it on the ground with the client and inform him, in general terms, how suitable it is for his purposes. An early meeting in the field is desirable because there is much for the aspirant owner to learn that cannot be understood well from reading alone. The consultant can point out on the land his reasons for the recommendations he makes. Such a meeting should serve to cement mutual confidence and understanding. It should not prove surprising if the forester immediately informs the client that his plans or objectives need substantial modification for successful attainment.

One of the obligations of a consultant is to make clear to the client whether or not his services will really be worth what they will cost. If the area involved is small, he may refer the prospective owner to public forestry agencies. Here the reader may wonder why he should not go to the public forester in the first place and get the consulting services free or at nominal cost. He can do so, but he should not expect the intensive and intimate type of help and advice that may be needed from men employed to serve the public welfare rather than the personal welfare of a client.

THE ATTORNEY

The attorney's advice will be needed on contracts for land purchase and sale of timber, for examining title abstracts and rendering an opinion, for clearing faulty titles, for advice on establishing ownership and protecting a title, on the desirability of incorporating, and on many related legal questions.

As stated earlier, an attorney in the county where the property is located is in a position to provide a variety of additional services because of his intimate acquaintance with county and town officers and local forest owners and timber operations. The individual's personal lawyer is prepared to provide recommendations on local lawyers. Also, local banks and businessmen can furnish references. Judges may also be consulted.

If the attorney is to serve his client in the most helpful manner, both he and the consultant forester may need to have detailed information on the client's personal situation. Both can be relied upon to respect confidences.

THE ACCOUNTANT

From the details of Chapter II, it should be clear that appropriate records kept according to generally accepted accounting practices are important. Unless the forest owner has had adequate accounting training, he should hire an accountant to record his transactions. Such records can readily be understood by other accountants. A certified public accountant's signature on the books carries weight with tax examiners and the courts. Books may need posting and closing only once a year unless a considerable volume of business is transacted.

The greatest value of the accountant, however, is to provide the owner with the necessary information about the financial side of his business. Such information can be the basis for important decisions that may determine the financial success or failure of the forest enterprise.

OTHER EXPERT SERVICES

The need for title examination should be clear from Chapter IV, and a local attorney may recommend one. The title examiner traces the ownership of the land in question back through the years as the record of such ownership, including mortgages, judgments, liens, etc., are recorded in the county clerk's record of deeds. A tax search also should be made, and both title examination and tax search should be examined by a lawyer. If there has been an unrecorded deed, the tax record may reveal it.

A land survey may be needed to locate boundaries accurately. Where low-value forest land is involved, general agreement by adjacent owners may suffice in lieu of a costly survey of record. If the land is particularly valuable, a survey by a licensed surveyor may be worthwhile. The consulting forester can recommend suitable men.

STATE FORESTRY OFFICIALS

Listed below are the titles and addresses of state forestry officials who are able to offer advice concerning sources for obtaining further assistance in developing private forestry holdings.[1]

Alabama: State Forester, 64 N. Union St., Montgomery, Ala. 36104
Alaska: State Forester, 344 Sixth Ave., Anchorage, Alaska 99501
Arizona: State Forester, 422 Office Bldg. E, Phoenix, Ariz. 85005
Arkansas: State Forester, P.O. Box 1940, Little Rock, Ark. 72203
California: State Forester, Resources Bldg., Sacramento, Calif. 95814
Colorado: State Forester, Colo. State Univ., Fort Collins, Colo. 80521
Connecticut: State Forester, 165 Capitol Ave., Hartford, Conn. 06103
Delaware: State Forester, 317 S. State St., Dover, Del. 19901
Florida: State Forester, P.O. Box 1200, Tallahassee, Fla. 32304
Georgia: Forestry Director, P.O. Box 1077, Macon, Ga. 31203
Hawaii: State Forester, 400 S. Beretania St., Honolulu, Hawaii 96813
Idaho: State Forester, 801 Capital Blvd., Boise, Idaho 83701
Illinois: State Forester, 400 S. Spring St., Springfield, Ill. 62706
Indiana: State Forester, 607 State Office Bldg., Indianapolis, Ind. 46209
Iowa: State Forester, E. 7th and Court Sts., Des Moines, Iowa 50309
Kansas: Extension Forester, Kansas State College, Manhattan, Kan. 66504
Kentucky: Forestry Director, New Capitol Annex, Frankfort, Ky. 40601
Louisiana: State Forester, P.O. Box 15239, Baton Rouge, La. 70815
Maine: Forest Commissioner, Maine Forestry Dept., Augusta, Me. 04330
Maryland: State Forester, State Office Bldg., Annapolis, Md. 21401
Massachusetts: Forest Director, 15 Ashburton Place, Boston, Mass. 02108
Michigan: State Forester, Steven T. Mason Bldg., Lansing, Mich. 48926
Minnesota: Forestry Director, Centennial Ofc. Bldg., St. Paul, Minn. 55101
Mississippi: State Forester, 1106 Woolfolk Bldg., Jackson, Miss. 39201
Missouri: State Forester, P.O. Box 180, Jefferson City, Mo. 65102
Montana: State Forester, 2705 Spurgin Rd., Missoula, Mont. 59801
Nebraska: State Forester, University of Nebraska, Lincoln, Neb. 68508
Nevada: State Forester, 201 S. Fall St., Carson City, Nev. 89701
New Hampshire: Resources Director, State Ofc. Bldg., Concord, N.H. 03033
New Jersey: State Forester, Labor & Industry Bldg., Trenton, N.J. 08611

[1] This list adapted from *Forests Forever* (pamphlet) (Washington, D.C.: U.S. Government Printing Office, 1966).

New Mexico: State Forester, P.O. Box 2167, Santa Fe, N.M. 87501
New York: Director, Div. of Lands and Forests, Albany, N.Y. 12183
North Carolina: State Forester, P.O. Box 2719, Raleigh, N.C. 27602
North Dakota: State Forester, State Sch. of Forestry, Bottineau, N.D. 58318
Ohio: Chief, Forestry Div., 815 Ohio Depts. Bldg., Columbus, Ohio 43215
Oklahoma: Forestry Director, Capitol Bldg., Oklahoma City, Okla. 74074
Oregon: State Forester, P.O. Box 2289, Salem, Ore. 97310
Pennsylvania: State Forester, Bureau of Forests, Harrisburg, Pa. 17120
Puerto Rico: Commonwealth Forester, P.O. Box 10163, Santurce, San Juan, P.R.
Rhode Island: Chief Forester, 83 Park St., Providence, R.I. 02903
South Carolina: State Forester, 5500 Broad River Rd., Columbia, S.C. 29202
South Dakota: State Forester, Pierre, S.D. 57501
Tennessee: State Forester, 2611 W. End Ave., Nashville, Tenn. 37203
Texas: Director, Texas Forest Service, College Station, Tex. 77843
Utah: State Forester, 525 W. 1300 South, Salt Lake City, Utah 84115
Vermont: Director of Forests, Montpelier, Vt. 05601
Virginia: State Forester, P.O. Box 3347, Charlottesville, Va. 22902
Washington: Forestry Supervisor, P.O. Box 110, Olympia, Wash. 98501
West Virginia: State Forester, Dept. of Natural Resources, Charleston, W. Va. 25305
Wisconsin: State Forester, P.O. Box 450, Madison, Wis. 53701
Wyoming: State Forester, Capitol Bldg., Cheyenne, Wyo. 82001

# ANNOTATED BIBLIOGRAPHY

Inasmuch as the interested landowner may wish to add some forestry books of lasting value to his own library, he should consider acquiring several good standard works for basic reference purposes, in addition to more simplified or popularized books and pamphlets. Three book companies have published forestry series: the largest, with some twenty-six volumes, is issued by the McGraw-Hill Book Company; the one by John Wiley & Sons is second largest with five titles; and The Ronald Press series, with a growing number of titles, is third. Nearly all of the books in these series were written as texts for college students preparing themselves for the forestry profession. However, with reasonable diligence by the interested reader they are not difficult to comprehend if one's educational background has included some training in mathematics, biology, physics, and chemistry. These books are most useful in presenting general knowledge of the basic principles and considerations relating to forest management, but there are also other understandings of importance to those who may be interested in responsible conservation generally. A number of other useful books pertaining to forestry are also available.

The following annotated listing presents available books and other literature deemed particularly useful to the forest owner who wishes to become well informed. Only a few of the more pertinent references for each of the several subject fields of forestry are given. These, and additional literature available in the better bookstores and libraries, should be examined carefully by the reader to determine their suitability for specific needs.

Books of a General Nature

An Introduction to American Forestry, 3rd ed., Shirley Allen and Grant Sharpe (New York: McGraw-Hill Book Co., 1950). This is a good introductory book for the layman or the entering student in forestry or for institutions giving a comprehensive introductory course in forestry. The book gives some historical background and is aimed more at the general reader than at the forestry practitioner. The authors, in 1967, were respectively professor emeritus and professor of forestry at the School of Natural Resources, University of Michigan.

Essentials of Forestry Practice, Charles H. Stoddard (New York: Ronald Press, 1959). This is a helpful book with which to start because it covers the various aspects of forestry in an introductory and informative manner. The author is a forest economist who formerly operated a correspondence course in the essentials of forestry. He has served government as chief of the Bureau of Land Management in the U.S. Department of the Interior.

Forestry and Its Career Opportunities, 2nd ed., Hardy L. Shirley (New York: McGraw-Hill Book Co., 1964). This book, intended as a text for an introductory course in forestry, stresses the historical, economic, and world setting of forestry in an overview manner. It also treats the development of the profession and employment outlook. It covers the field of forest products, forest recreation, and forest economics in somewhat more detail than the two texts listed above.

Trees (Yearbook of Agriculture) (Washington, D.C.: U.S. Government Printing Office, 1949). This is a book meant for general reading covering a wide variety of subjects relating to forestry including history, famous individual trees, shade and ornamental trees, forest ecology, tree planting, small woodlots, industrial forestry, national forests, multiple use of forests, protection of forests against fire, insects, and diseases, recreation, wildlife, forest products, and forestry outlook. Similar yearbooks on soils and other agricultural subjects are also available.

The Great Forest, Richard G. Lillard (New York: Alfred A. Knopf, 1947). This entertaining volume describes the forest as it was first discovered by the white man in America and discusses the ways it has changed since that time. It is a readable book for the layman and contains much factual information of interest.

Forest and Range Policy, Samuel Dana, dean emeritus, School of Natural Resources, University of Michigan (New York: McGraw-Hill Book Co., 1956). This book deals particularly with the various land laws and federal and state administrative practices as they were developed for forestry in the United States. It is primarily for the student who wants to understand the background of American forestry and the leadership taken by the federal government in developing forestry.

Reference Handbooks

A Woodsman's Manual, Austin Cary (Cambridge: Harvard University Press, 1932). The author was one of the first practical woodsmen to systematize the information on forestry for the benefit of the private practitioner and owner. Although this book carries a fourth edition, 1932 dateline, much of the information in it is highly useful today. It is easily read and understood by the layman.

Forestry Handbook, Reginald D. Forbes and Arthur B. Meyer, eds., (New York: Ronald Press, 1955). This is a comprehensive handbook meant for reference use by practicing foresters. Not all of the information in it can be used effectively by the uninitiated, but a great deal of it is given in sufficient detail for the generally informed reader. It is a useful book to have available in the library of any forest owner; and if only one book can be purchased, this is the one the estate owner should have.

Wood Handbook, U.S. Department of Agriculture, Forest Products Laboratory, Madison, Wisconsin. For sale by Superintendent of Documents, U.S. Government Printing Office, Washington, D.C. Current edition. This is the standard reference source for detailed basic information on different wood species as materials for construction, with data for uses of wood in design and specifications.

Tree Farm Business Management, James M. Vardaman (New York: Ronald Press, 1965). This book is prepared for the small-to medium-sized woodland owner with emphasis on southern United States conditions. It covers forest management, forest accounts, and forest law. Emphasis is on management for financial returns.

Timber and Forest Products Law, Harry W. Falk, (Berkeley, Calif.: Howell-North Press, 1958). This volume provides comprehensive treatment for the professional forester in layman's language. It is a useful book for men with a legal bent who own or manage forest properties to sell forest products.

Forest Resources and Timber Demand

The U.S. Forest Service is required by law to maintain a continuing national inventory of our forest resources. Periodic reports are issued on a state-by-state basis. About once each decade a nationwide report is published. This is a comprehensive appraisal of the present forest land area, volume of standing timber, growth rate, and current timber used. It also offers estimates of future timber requirements and prospects for meeting them. The latest detailed national timber resource review was published in 1958 under the title *Timber Resources for America's Future* (Forest Resource *Report No. 14,* Washington D.C., 713 pp.). The most recent appraisal of the timber supply and demand outlook is given in *Timber Trends in the United States,* Forest Resource *Report No. 17* (1965), 235 pp. Reports covering the inventory situation in various states are available from the U.S. Forest Service and may be more current for specific areas.

Proceedings of the Fifth American Forest Congress, October 28-30, 1963, Washington, D.C. (Washington, D.C.: American Forestry Association, 1964). This includes numerous papers, mostly of a general nature, dealing with forest resource management, research and survey, and forest land protection. Many of the papers will make interesting reading for forest owners concerned about opinion on forestry and forest policy.

Economic Aspects of Forestry

Economics of American Forestry, Albert C. Worrell (New York: John Wiley & Sons, 1959). This is a readable text dealing with the application of economic concepts to forestry situations and problems. It provides a straightforward treatment of investment decisions that should be rather easily understood by the informed general reader. The author is professor of forestry economics at Yale University.

The Small Private Forest in the United States, Charles H. Stoddard (Washington, D.C.: Resources for the Future, 1958). This book analyzes the economic problems faced by the small forest landowner, and with economies of size in timber growing as a financial enterprise. It also deals with various measures to modify unfavorable factors and, hence, to make forest ownership more attractive financially.

Resources in America's Future, Hans H. Landsberg, Leonard L. Fischman, and Joseph L. Fisher (Baltimore: Johns Hopkins Press, 1963). This book discusses the major land resources, crops, lumber and pulpwood, water, minerals, fuels, metals, chemicals, and the demands being made upon them for human use, including recreation. It forecasts the future requirements for paper, lumber, and other forest products and weighs these against the requirements for other basic resources projected forward to the year 2000. The authors are employed by the foundation Resources for the Future, and one of them, Joseph Fisher, is its president.

The Economic Importance of Timber in the United States, Dwight Hair, U.S. Forest Service, *Miscellaneous Publication 941* (Washington, D.C., 1963). This publication covers the general importance of the timber industry in the national economy and discusses the likelihood of its continuing to play a key role in the future.

Fundamentals of Forestry Economics, William A. Duerr (New York: McGraw-Hill Book Co., 1960). This is a somewhat sophisticated treatment of the subject that presupposes some knowledge of current economic theory. Those with a background in economics may prefer it to the other mentioned.

Trees and Their Treatment

Textbook of Dendrology, 3rd ed., William M. Harlow and Elwood S. Harrar (New York: McGraw-Hill Book Co., 1950). Dendrology deals with the identification of trees and their importance to man. This is an authoritative reference covering the important forest trees of the United States and Canada. It includes tree range and maps and photographs of flowers, fruit, leaves, and bark, real aids to accurate tree identification by the layman. William Harlow also offers a simpler treatment, *Trees of the Eastern and Central United States and Canada* (New York: Dover Company, 1957).

North American Trees, Richard J. Preston (Ames: Iowa State College Press, 1950). This book is a concise but well-illustrated manual for tree identification, habitats, and general silvical characteristics of most of our tree species. Dr. Preston is director of the Division of Forestry at North Carolina State College.

The Principles of Silviculture, Fred S. Baker (New York: McGraw-Hill Book Co., 1950). Silviculture deals with the cultural treatment of trees and stands to promote their best growth and utility. Baker's book provides comprehensive treatment of the biological and ecological basis for forest stand development and the principles that apply.

Regional Silviculture of the United States, John W. Barrett, ed. (New York: Ronald Press, 1962). This current compilation by numerous authorities in eleven major regions of the United States brings into readable perspective the silvicultural practices recommended for tree species and timber stands as influenced by significant biological, physical, market, and general economic circumstances of the region.

Forest Ecology, Stephen H. Spurr (Ann Arbor, Mich.: Ann Arbor Publications, 1962). This is an up-to-date text dealing with the ecological aspects of silviculture, which is mostly applied forest ecology. This book offers sound treatment of the dynamics of relationships operative among natural forces in the forest community.

Management of Forests and Forest Lands

Management of forest lands involves many types of capabilities and understanding where detailed preparation is usually required for competent performance. It is for this reason that professional forestry schools are maintained. Major segments of forest management responsibility deal with such essentials as valuation and appraisal of land and timber, with the regulatory planning and scheduling of timber harvests, with surveying and land measurement, inventory assessment and control, with use of aerial photographs as managerial and planning aids, with contracts and business and economic matters, and similar considerations of practical managerial concern. A variety of helpful books is available in each of these fields of management. Some are listed below.

Most books on forest management are written for use as texts in professional courses at forestry colleges. Also, since management of forest resources must have responsible continuity to be meaningful, these books are written usually with the large timberland holding in view where investment commitment has greater assurance of sustained support, such as public land ownerships and the holdings of larger corporations. They do, however, contain important information of value to the forest owner with modest-sized holdings. In addition, there are a few books that deal more specifically with forest management questions on smaller ownerships, as noted below.

Applied Forest Management, Paul E. Bruns (Ann Arbor, Mich.: Edwards Brothers, Inc., 1954). This is a very readable and practically oriented book on forest management written for those in the field concerned with professional practice and interpretation of technical principles into actual managerial accomplishment. Professor Bruns heads the Forestry Department at the University of New Hampshire, Durham.

Woodland Management, W. E. Hiley (London: Faber and Faber, Ltd.,

1955). Distributed in the United States by John de Graff, Inc., New York. This book deals with the practical management of woodlands as an enterprise and provides a large amount of realistic information on the many facets of forest estate operation. The style is only moderately technical. It is, of course, related to the markets, social structure, and other circumstances prevailing in England, but the adjustment to United States conditions is usually possible for the informed reader.

American Forest Management, Kenneth P. Davis (New York: McGraw-Hill Book Co., Inc., 1954). This college text is the most comprehensive professional treatment of the subject. It includes major sections on growth, harvest schedules, and land and timber valuation and appraisal. Dr. Davis is professor of forest management in the Yale School of Forestry.

Forest Management, 2nd ed., H. Arthur Meyer, A. B. Recknagel, D. D. Stevenson, R. A. Bartoo (New York: Ronald Press, 1961). A readable presentation is offered here, covering problems of organizing the property, classification of lands, and use of growth data in planning timber management as a business enterprise. It also discusses in detail the methods of regulating the harvest of wood products and offers several examples of management plans used on industrial and public properties.

A Forestry Venture, W. E. Hiley (London: Faber and Faber, Ltd., 1964). This is a readable account of the management of a specific forest property in southern England. It deals in a realistic way with how the forest manager met his many day-to-day problems during both war-time and peace.

Forest Valuation, H. H. Chapman and W. H. Meyer (New York: McGraw-Hill Book Co., 1947). This is an older but still sound text on the businessman's approach to appraisal and utility of a forested property, including chapters on market values of forest property, taxation, damage appraisal, insurance, and investment risks.

Elementary Surveying, 4th ed., Russell C. Brinker and Warren C. Taylor (Scranton, Pa.: International Book Co., 1962). This volume provides basic information and methods for land measurements, boundary surveys, map preparation, ground layout of common structures, photo steroscopy, and related subject areas. It was prepared as a textbook for instruction of foresters and engineers but is sufficiently readable for the well-informed layman.

Aerial Photographic Interpretation, Donald R. Lueder (New York: McGraw-Hill Book Co., 1959). This is a well-illustrated and comprehensible book covering principles and applications of photoanalysis and photo reading and interpretation for forestry, engineering, land forms, agricultural and land use studies, urban and regional planning, and vegetative mapping. Aerial photographs of most land areas are available for use at county soil conservation district or county agent offices.

Forest Measurement

Forest measurement, or mensuration, deals with the important subjects of estimating timber volume, timber quality, timber growth rates and predictions, cull and defect, and the merchantable volume of lumber to be cut from trees and logs. It is a technical subject requiring considerable mathematical understanding. Also, because of the numbers of trees involved, mensuration must make use of statistically controlled estimates in many instances, rather than the actual measurements common to normal inventorying of raw materials in other types of productive enterprise. In addition, careful interpretation of aerial photographs is deeply involved in modern timber inventory methods. The following books should be examined by the individual to check their utility for him.

Forest Mensuration, 3rd ed., Donald Bruce and Francis X. Schumacker (New York: McGraw-Hill Book Co., 1950). This is a standard college textbook on methods of direct measurement of trees and stands for volume, age, and growth, methods of estimating by sampling, and ways of predicting growth and yield. Some of the chapters are rather technical, but the authors present basic concepts in ways that are generally understandable.

Forest Mensuration, H. Arthur Meyer (State College, Pa.: Penns Valley Publishers, Inc., 1953). This is a more readable presentation of forest mensuration with wider application of modern approaches, including land measures and boundary survey by use of aerial photos. It provides introductory coverage of forest statistical concepts, measurement of logs and trees, forest inventories, growth determination, and the more commonly used log rules.

Protection of Forests

Protection of forests includes protection against fire, insects, tree diseases, animals, weather, and other destructive agents. It is well for the forest owner to have a book of general reference on these subjects. He will normally, however, look to his state forest fire protective organization to protect his lands against fire and against tree diseases and insect outbreaks of major proportion. Many of the losses that occur in the forest, however, are relatively inconspicuous, especially those caused by disease, and are accepted by the timberland owner as inevitable, and little action is taken to minimize them. Having a suitable reference book at hand, however, may enable the forest owner to recognize them and to minimize the damage they cause. The following books are suggested:

Forest Pathology, 3rd ed., John S. Boyce (New York: McGraw-Hill Book Co., 1961). A scholarly treatment of tree disease organisms by a biological scientist. Feasible control lies mostly in maintaining optimum vigor in forest stands through proper management.

Insect Enemies of Eastern Forests, F. C. Craighead, U.S. Department of Agriculture, *Miscellaneous Publication 657* (Washington, D.C.: U.S. Government Printing Office, 1950); also, for western forests: *Misc. Pub. 273.* This government publication treats in a practical manner the more important forest insects and their control, including recommended adjustment of timber management practices. Frequently, natural forces take care of control satisfactorily. Before engaging in extensive insect control, the forest owner should consult with his local state forestry office about the need and latest methods.

Forest Fires—Control and Use, Kenneth P. Davis (New York: McGraw-Hill Book Co., 1959). This is an excellent authoritative treatment of forest fire behavior, effects, and control. The forest owner here will be interested more in the effects from burning the woods and the use of fire as a silvicultural tool than in the specific measures and methods of controlling forest fires. The latter is a task for the public foresters in his locality.

Wildlife Management, Reuben Trippensee (New York: McGraw-Hill Book Co., 1948). Although this book deals primarily with the management of game and furbearers, there is useful information in it for the forest owner. Wildlife, especially deer and porcupines, commonly cause extensive damage to forest stands when populations are not kept within reasonable limits. The original classic treatment of wildlife management is by Aldo Leopold in his *Game Management,* published in 1933 by Scribner.

Forest Products and Logging

It is from the sale of forest products that the forest owner obtains the money for paying his costs. To aid his understanding of values and marketability of trees, it is well that he know something about forest products and the industries that manufacture them. These industries are primarily sawmills, pulp and paper mills, and wood conversion plants. There are also numerous minor wood-using industries that may be important locally. Lumber is generally the most important product of the forest and, hence, deserves primary consideration.

Lumber, 2nd ed., Nelson C. Brown and James S. Bethel (New York : John Wiley & Sons, 1958). This is a practical book covering the general subject of lumber, its manufacture, sale, and use. The senior author is professor emeritus of forest products at the State University College of Forestry at Syracuse University, and the junior author is dean of forestry at the University of Washington.

Forest Products, Their Sources, Production and Utilization, 2nd ed., A. J. Panshin, E. S. Harrar, W. J. Baker, and T. B. Proctor (New York: McGraw-Hill Book Co., 1962). This book covers the subject of forest products in a thorough manner and includes a chapter on plywood and veneers and one on pulp and paper technology as well as other chemical products and derived products.

Logging, Nelson C. Brown (New York: John Wiley & Sons, 1949). The average forest owner is more likely to be interested in and concerned with logging than with lumber manufacture, secondary forest products, or pulp and paper manufacture. He may actually engage in logging, himself. Brown's book covers logging methods and operating considerations common to the somewhat traditional practice of timber harvest.

Harvesting Timber Crops, 2nd ed., A. E. Wackerman, A. S. Mitchell, W. D. Hagenstein (New York: McGraw-Hill Book Co., 1966). This book presents the most up-to-date practical explanation of correct timber cutting, logging, and harvesting methods, with emphasis upon costs and relationships to timber-growing considerations. It includes chapters on harvest planning, labor and safety provisions, measurement of forest products, and record keeping. It is well illustrated and very readable.

The Northeastern Logger's Handbook, U.S. Department of Agriculture *Handbook No. 6,* January, 1951 (Washington, D.C.: U.S. Government Printing Office). This is a handbook prepared for use not by forestry students but by the actual logging operator. It is simple, well illustrated, and direct. The methods proposed apply largely to conditions in the eastern and southern United States.

A number of detailed treatises on logging methods also have been published by the Canadian Pulp and Paper Association, Woodlands Section, Montreal, prepared by Alexander Koroleff.

Forest Recreation

Several pamphlets recently have been written on the construction of picnic grounds, campgrounds, and other recreational projects both for personal use and for commercial use. Some treat these as self-supporting business enterprises. These have been published by agricultural experiment stations, by the U.S. Forest Service, by other agencies of the Department of Agriculture, by agencies of the U.S. Department of the Interior, and some by consultants and other authors. Many of these are available through the local district forester or agricultural county agent's office.